AGRICULTURAL CRISIS
IN AMERICA

A Reference Handbook

Other Titles in ABC-CLIO's
CONTEMPORARY WORLD ISSUES
Series

Books in the Contemporary World Issues series address vital issues in today's society such as terrorism, sexual harassment, homelessness, AIDS, gambling, animal rights, and air pollution. Written by professional writers, scholars, and nonacademic experts, these books are authoritative, clearly written, up-to-date, and objective. They provide a good starting point for research by high school and college students, scholars, and general readers, as well as by legislators, businesspeople, activists, and others.

Each book, carefully organized and easy to use, contains an overview of the subject; a detailed chronology; biographical sketches; facts and data and/or documents and other primary-source material; a directory of organizations and agencies; annotated lists of print and nonprint resources; a glossary; and an index.

Readers of books in the Contemporary World Issues series will find the information they need in order to better understand the social, political, environmental, and economic issues facing the world today.

AGRICULTURAL CRISIS
IN AMERICA

A Reference Handbook

Dana L. Hoag

**CONTEMPORARY
WORLD ISSUES**

ABC-CLIO

Santa Barbara, California
Denver, Colorado
Oxford, England

146919

Library of Congress Cataloging in Publication Data

Hoag, Dana L.
    Agricultural crisis in America : a reference handbook / Dana L. Hoag.
        p.   cm. — (Contemporary world issues)
    Includes bibliographical references and index.
    ISBN 0-87436-737-9 (alk. paper)
        1. Agriculture and state—United States. 2. Agriculture—Economic
aspects—United States. 3. Agriculture—Environmental aspects—United
States. 4. Food supply—United States. I. Title. II. Series.

HD1761 .H56 1999
338.1'0973—dc21   99-052004

04 03 02 01 00   10 9 8 7 6 5 4 3 2   (cloth)

ABC-CLIO, Inc.
130 Cremona Drive, P.O. Box 1911
Santa Barbara, California 93116-1911

This book is printed on acid-free paper ∞ .

"Agriculture confronts the new century with challenges as demanding as those that shaped its turbulent course through the Twentieth Century. Today's agricultural interests are converging with those of rural communities and agribusinesses. Stewardship is now a joint enterprise with suburban residents. This book provides an excellent balance of perspectives on seven crises as well as insights to cooperative solutions."

Louis Swanson
Head, Department of Sociology
Colorado State University
April 1999

To my family:
Laura, Brian, Timothy, and Andy,
and to my mother, Jeanne.

Contents

Preface

Seven agricultural crises are examined in this book: (1) Farm and Ranch Survivability, (2) Modernization, (3) Feeding a Growing World, (4) Safe Food and Drinking Water, (5) Stewardship and the Environment, (6) Urbanization and Land Use, and (7) Country and Urban Conflicts. Not having enough food would be disastrous indeed. However, most agricultural crises are far less dramatic. Agriculture finds itself in crisis for the most part because it has to change. Modernization, for example, has brought countless benefits to farmers[1] and consumers alike. We have more food at less cost, produced on less land, and with fewer farmers. However, changes to accommodate modernization have come at a cost. Farmers and their families have been uprooted from their land and traditions as fewer people are needed to produce our food. And high-tech farming methods that rely more on chemicals and genetic engineering raise new concerns about threats to human health and the environment. While Americans may not go hungry anytime soon, these "crises of change," so to speak, will capture Americans' attention for years to come.

---

[1] In some cases, the terms *farm, ranch,* and *agriculture* are used interchangeably to facilitate writing and to match the way many agricultural statistics are reported.

The purpose of this book is to examine the seven crises identified above. A battleground of ideas has emerged as each person tries to advance his or her own agenda about how agriculture should or should not change. So far, Americans have not settled on a shared vision. Therefore, as much information as possible is presented here about the scope and diversity of each crisis.

Chapter 1 discusses tradition and change related to each crisis. The chapter concludes with a discussion on society and government. The chronology of events leading up to modern-day crises is given in Chapter 2. Biographies of important figures related to the seven crises are presented in Chapter 3. More than 50 facts, figures, charts, and case studies are provided for each of the seven crises in Chapter 4. These exhibits provide far more information than can be discussed here. If you want to look further, Chapters 5, 6, and 7, respectively, list organizations, print resources, and nonprint resources that will lead you to more details about any of these crises. Finally, a glossary of terms is provided at the end of the book.

Acknowledgments

Thanks to my wife Laura and my three sons, Brian, Timothy, and Andy, for taking care of all the things at home that I neglected while working on this book.

Thanks also to the following people who helped me gather and sort through mounds of information—Brian Hoag, Polly Grant, Jodie Walker, Miriam Hammer, and Elizabeth Garner—and to Louis Swanson and Andy Seidl for proofreading.

Finally, thanks to the folks at ABC-CLIO, especially Kristi Ward and Martha Whitt.

Cultivating Change and Crisis

1

A mericans have a rich agricultural history, with deep roots and strong traditions. Most country folk would find it hard to imagine why anyone would want to change agricultural traditions. Yet, change better describes American agriculture than does tradition. Changes in how we grow food started way back when the Pilgrims arrived in America. Native Americans were already cultivating crops here, but with the arrival of the Pilgrims, their agricultural traditions were changed forever. The Pilgrims were risk takers, seeking change from their previous lives. They crossed the Atlantic to a place they had never seen, where they did not know how to farm, where laws and politics were unsettled, and where the intentions of native peoples were unknown. But come they did, bringing change and creating crises for anyone who did not wish to (or who could not) change with them. And agriculture has continued to grow and change ever since; the tractor replaced horses, we rely more heavily every year on technological improvements in chemicals and genetics, and farms just keep getting larger and larger.

The success of American agriculture is truly remarkable. In the 1800s, four out of five people had to work on farms and ranches to sustain the nation's basic food needs. Today only a tiny fraction of our population, just 1 in 50, is required to supply everything we need two times over.

It is our success, however, that presents a paradox. Our willingness to explore new ideas, to change, and to adapt gives us success—but the success then establishes a tradition that people don't want to change. American traditions are constantly challenged by new ideas. Most recently, society is challenging the notion that abundant production is the best measure of good farming. Americans have the income and luxury to demand animal rights, better conditions for laborers, and production methods that are friendlier to the environment. These new demands stress established traditions and introduce input from "outsiders" that have traditionally not had a say in how agriculture conducts its business.

Tradition, Change, and Crisis

It is important to appreciate the strong grasp that tradition has on agriculture because *crises occur when traditions are threatened.* The more deeply rooted the tradition, the harder it is to change. "People believe that society is disintegrating when it can no longer be pictured in familiar terms," said American lawyer Thurman Arnold. Economist John Kenneth Galbraith warned that when "faced with the choice between changing one's mind and proving that there is no need to do so, almost everybody gets busy on the proof."

Agriculture frequently experiences crisis because it is always changing. However, today's tradition was yesterday's change. Therefore, what is today's change will be tomorrow's tradition. Many things that we accept today were crises to those who had to change before us. For example, there was a time when farmers that had to supplement their incomes were seen as failures. Now most producers accept that some income will come from off the farm.

Tradition is very important to agriculture, but it is hard to ignore all the positive things that have come from change, too. Change is always hard, but it won't feel so much like a crisis if the new outcome is preferred to the old. *The most important crisis facing agriculture today is that Americans cannot agree about where we ought to go.*

Some people want more technology, some want less; using chemicals to produce crops is fine for some people and a catastrophe to others; some people think family farms are important, others don't really care whether a corporation provides their food. Eating animals is a moral outrage to some people, and some people fear that environmental degradation is threatening our ability to survive. How can we cope with change when we can't even agree about an important topic like whether biotechnology is an appropriate way to feed a growing population?

The "Agrarian" Tradition

Agriculture has enjoyed a positive image for a long time. For example, in a 1995 survey more than 80 percent of Coloradans said that agriculture was very important to their quality of life (Wallace 1995). Americans have consistently said that they care enough about farmers and ranchers to be willing to pay higher taxes, or to grant them special rights (Barlett 1993). In the Wallace survey, nearly 90 percent of the respondents were willing to provide public support for environmental conservation. In a different survey, over half of the people surveyed said that protecting open space on private ranches was important simply to know that it exists or to help the local farm economy (Rosenberger, Walsh, and McKean 1996). Half of the respondents were willing to pay $60 or more per year to help ranches keep ranching, rather than let the land go idle or into vacation homes.

This country's esteem for agriculture has been recorded in the words of noted poets, storytellers, and essayists such as Ralph Waldo Emerson, Henry David Thoreau, and Wendell Berry. Politicians use America's love of agriculture to stir passion in their constituents. Protecting agriculture is "good for all people" and, consequently, good for politicians since "farmers are the backbone of America." But why do farmers and ranchers command such high esteem in our country? Why is the public so willing to support farmers and ranchers when other businesses fail at much higher rates?

Our reverence for agriculture in the United States is most likely not driven by a fear that without farms we won't have food. Rather, it reflects an appreciation or love for life on the farm. If it was the food that people were concerned about, as opposed to the farmers that produce the food, we would not have supported small farmers with our taxes and our hearts for as long as we have. About 15 percent of farmers can supply 85 percent of our food, yet society continues to support the majority of farmers who supply only 15 percent of our food.

Thomas Jefferson's writings about agrarian values over 200 years ago continue to be widely quoted:

> Cultivators of the earth are the most valuable citizens. They are the most vigorous, the most independent, the most virtuous, and they are tied to their country and wedded to its liberty and interests by the most lasting bonds.

A kind of "Agrarian Ideology" evolved out of this and other writings by Jefferson that places farmers on a pedestal, deserving of our esteem and protection. The Agrarian Ideology states that

> agriculture is the most important occupation of humankind; rural life is morally superior; and a nation of small independent farmers is better for democracy.

Wendell Berry (1987) stressed that self-interest on farms was consistent with community interests because honesty and integrity, which are needed for community, are required of family farms. If we lose the "family" in family farms, it is no longer necessary to be ethical and honest. Berry and Jefferson were expressing what many still feel today: living in a rural area is a better way of life that builds stronger character and better people. The modern version of these beliefs that many people still hold includes:

- Farming is not only a business, it's a way of life.
- It is better for a family than a corporation to own a farm.
- Land should be owned by the person who tills it.
- Farmers should be their own bosses.
- Anyone that wants to farm should be able to.
- Farmers should be protected.
- Farmers are more ethical, more honest, and harder workers.
- Farm property rights are more sacred than others because of the importance of what farmers do with their land.
- Rural people are more patriotic.

What do you believe? Are farmers more virtuous? Are rural areas safer places because people are more honest? Are there fewer teen pregnancies, acts of violence, or other ills of city life? In 1944, Walter Goldschmidt expressed his belief, based on his study of two California communities, that communities dominated by industrial farms have lower standards of living and a poorer quality of life (Browne et al. 1992). His conclusions, cited for decades, were bolstered by a 1988 study of industrialized states by Dean MacCannell for the U.S. Office of Technology Assessment (OTA). The weight of evidence, however, contradicts these two studies (Browne et al. 1992). Four other studies by the OTA, for example, found no evidence that social and economic well-being are associated with farm structure.

Regardless of whether farming is or is not the "backbone" of America, there are many reasons to continue to support agriculture. Perhaps we are shifting from a society that sympathizes with farmers because we envy their lives to a society that cares about farmers because it is in our own self-interest. Castle (1995) suggests that we should care about rural residents and farmers because we will all be better off. Rural and urban areas are increasingly dependent upon one another and sometimes difficult to tell apart. A majority of rural farmers get most of their incomes from off the farm. And most of the nation's wildlife habitat, forests, wetlands, and other natural resources that people enjoy are under the stewardship of farmers and rural citizens.

A Changing Agriculture

There is no question that agriculture has changed dramatically over the last 200 years. Perhaps it is changing even faster than ever before. As shown in Table 1 on page 6, since 1940 one-third as many producers operate farms that are three times larger. Farmers now total less than 1 percent of our population, yet each one feeds almost 140 people. American farmers feed and clothe twice as many people at the same cost to society than we did over 50 years ago. While accomplishing this, the value of exports is nearly 75 times higher (over sixfold in real terms) today than it was in 1940.

Agriculture is changing in other ways, too. The stereotypical farm, like the one where Dorothy lived in the movie *The Wizard of Oz*, has all but disappeared. Modernization has produced precision farming and biotechnology that can introduce genes from one organism to another. Some people predict that the days of delivering number 2 yellow corn to the local grain elevator for processing

Table 1: Change in Farm and Ranch Characteristics 1940–Present

Characteristic	1940	1998
Farm Size	135 acres	469 acres
Number of Farms	6.1 million	2 million
Farm Populations	31 million (23%)	2 million (0.6%)
People Fed per Farm	22	139
Value of Farm Products	$21 billion ($244 in '98 dollars)	$226 billion
Value of Product Exported	$0.7 billion ($8.5 in '98 dollars)	$54.7 billion
Net Farm Income	$5 billion ($59 in '98 dollars)	$55 billion

and distribution could end in as soon as five years. In the future, farmers might deliver specialty corn tailored for corn flakes, corn sweetener, feed for natural beef, feed for sheep, or corn grown especially for making plastics. And consumers now want more say about the way food is raised and handled so that the environment is protected, so food and water are safe to consume, and so that animals are well treated.

Farmers and nonfarmers alike are in awe about the knowledge explosion. New technology requires new knowledge and increased specialization to survive. Farmers have to make decisions about more complex issues, to rely on others such as outside consultants, and to get more insurance due to their decreased confidence about these decisions. The complexity of solutions is increased, too, by the need to satisfy new neighbors from the urban fringe that may not understand or agree with the way farmers have always done things.

The United States government is becoming increasingly aware of the need to study all these changes in agriculture and their effects on the population. In response, a division of the USDA known as the Cooperative State Research, Education, and Extension Service has recently created an educational initiative with the goal of "managing change in agriculture." According to a January 1997 report, "agriculture is in the midst of a major revolution that is bringing profound changes to how food is produced, processed, distributed, and marketed in the United States and abroad." Changes include:

- Dramatic change in federal farm programs, giving producers greater flexibility in management decisions and greater responsibility for marketing and risk management.
- Changing consumer preferences, as the U.S. population becomes older, more suburban, and more ethnically diverse, and as people demand greater variety, quality, safety, and convenience in an affordable food supply.
- Increased globalization of markets, providing more opportunities as well as more competition in domestic and foreign markets.
- Accelerated industrialization of agriculture, demanding greater coordination of successive stages in the production and distribution of food and fiber products.
- New technologies, often more complex and difficult to use effectively and profitably than earlier technologies and sometimes restricted to a limited number of users.
- Heightened expectations for environmental protection and natural resource conservation, with implications for management decisions of producers and processors.
- Increasingly powerful information systems, providing greater access to information for decisionmaking for some—but not all—people. (www.reeusda.gov/resd/ag_econ/mchg-02.htm)

The feeling that agriculture is in crisis was made worse by the federal government in 1996 when it took major steps to severely reduce financial supports that farm and ranch producers had come to rely on. The government had previously experimented with financial supports for several decades, but gradually most people became doubtful that the government could steer agriculture in a positive direction with a complex system of ambiguous, costly subsidies. In 1986, farm price and income supports alone totaled $26 billion to producers. Environmentalists tried to use the carrots provided by these payments to help producers form environmentally friendly farming habits. Nevertheless, by the mid-1990s, just about everyone agreed that these massive federal supports were not in the best interest of anyone; even farmers agreed, since without the programs they were better able to respond to the market. What farmers did not expect at this time was a crash of the Asian market, a drop in all exports, bumper crop supplies, and very low prices. Despite supposedly "ending the era of big government spending" with changes in the 1996 farm bill, the government ended up spending $16.6 billion in 1999 to help farmers (compared to $7.5 billion in 1997). Low farm prices forced the government to enact emergency relief programs and kicked in a clause from the farm bill that provided deficiency payments to make up the difference between the market prices and preset prices. Initially, government program costs stayed low when agriculture was doing well. However, without the programs, crop supplies swelled and output prices dropped by 11 percent from 1996 to 1999. Input prices rose by 2 percent over the same period. Net farm income fell from a high of $54.9 billion in 1996 to $44 billion in 1999. Although farmers are under increasing stress, they are not in as much financial trouble as they were in the mid-1980s. At $44 billion, net farm income in 1999 is comparable to the average for the decade, but one-third came from government supports.

Finally, on top of these conflicts, changes, and crises, farmers worldwide will have to feed about twice the current global population in the next half-century. And they will have to produce this food with highly dynamic and heterogeneous farms, with safer farming practices, with less damage to the environment, and without provoking conflicts with urban neighbors.

Cultivating agricultural change will require a good understanding about the source of problems, the influence of unique site conditions, some form of agreement about a desired direction, and effective and enforceable policies and institutions to move in the desired direction.

Seven Crises in Agriculture

Kinsey (1992) outlined seven trends driving U.S. food demands into the twenty-first century:

- **Slow growth in U.S. food demand**—Population growth rates in the United States are slow, and we use little of our income to purchase food. This will slow growth rates of agricultural commodities and intensify competition for value-added services.

- **Demand for more variety in the U.S.**—Niche marketing is growing and mass marketing of commodities is shrinking. Money can be made targeting foods to different consumer tastes, such as growing Asian immigrant communities.

- **Demand for more homogeneous products worldwide—**
Although we want more variety, other countries are catching
up to us, making us all a bit more similar. People in developing countries want the same things we want, like proteins in
meats.

- **Demand for convenience—**We are all a lot busier than we
were in the 1950s. Over 70 percent of American women of
childbearing age are in the paid labor force. Since the
majority of working women still report doing most of the
grocery shopping and cooking, people are looking a lot
more toward convenience. People buy mixed, cut vegetables
ready to cook rather than cutting and mixing them themselves. This is why the value-added industry has grown so
rapidly.

- **Demand for services from the public sector—**As we spend
more time out of the home and rely more on industry to pre-
prepare our food, we delegate more responsibility to the
government to assure us that our money is not wasted and
that our food is safe.

- **Demand for environmentally friendly goods—**People are
becoming increasingly aware of the environmental costs
related to their consumption. Many are willing to pay for
environmentally friendly products, such as organic, free
range, or hormone free.

- **Demand for healthier foods—**Health-conscious Americans
want fat-free, sugar-free, guilt-free products. This trend
provides food manufacturers with the opportunity to create
a broader line of products but does little for farmers and
ranchers.

Kinsey is concerned about food demand, and therefore her
ideas only scratch the surface about how agriculture is changing. I
found countless articles focused on the environment, on society,
on the rural economy, and on many other aspects of change. By
reading her study and many others, I have identified at least seven
potential crises.

The various dimensions and viewpoints about each crisis
are illustrated in each of the brief discussions below in as much
depth as possible. Nevertheless, I'm sure that I missed topics of
great importance to some people. Beef producers, for example,
are facing a serious crisis as they try to reinvent the industry to

recapture market share from other meats, to avoid being controlled by large corporations, and to maintain very important "cowboy" traditions. This topic receives very limited attention here due to a lack of space and its complexity. More detailed information about most, if not all, related topics can be found through the resources provided in Chapters 5, 6, and 7.

Crisis 1: Farm and Ranch Survivability

The disappearance of farms and farm people is probably the strongest felt of all agricultural crises in America. Farming today is very different than 20, 50, or 100 years ago. Ninety percent of the population lived on farms in the year 1800. In 1850, there were 15 million people living on 1.4 million farms. The number of farms peaked at around 7 million in the 1930s and has fallen ever since. At the end of the twentieth century, only 2 million farms remain, and the farm population has dwindled to under 2 percent of the total population in the United States.

Why Disappearing Farms Is a Crisis

The reason so many people feel that losing farms is a crisis is that many still support the agrarian ideologies described above. People are concerned that the farmers' way of life is a disappearing piece of Americana that is important to our rural economies and our nation's food security. Farming is more than a business to many people. Economics professor, Raymond Beneke (1998, p. 43), for example, wrote:

> Swan Lake, my home farm in Iowa, was more than 160 acres of land, a house and a set of farm buildings. It was more than its gently rolling terrain and its magnificent view high above the old lake bed. It was a special place, tranquil and secure, a value system and, later, a bundle of pleasant memories.

To Beneke, and many like him, his farm is his home. But *family* farming may now be on the endangered species list.

So what's wrong with corporations owning land instead of families? Wendell Berry (1987) gives a stirring description of what can happen when farm jobs are replaced with factory jobs. When a farmer owns his or her own land, he places value on being a good farmer, a skilled craftsman, and a good neighbor. His job is a lifestyle, not just a way to make money. However, when a person works for someone else or is a cog doing an insignificant task in a giant wheel, he is denied the use of his mind because he is not part of the final product. He is disconnected from the responsibility to the ultimate consumer. This process, called "dismemberment," is a distinction between making and doing and will lead to inferior products. Many of us, he points out, live to achieve unemployment. We live for weekends, and we want early retirement and long vacations. A family farmer in most cases places value on the work, not on the income it provides so he or she can do something else.

One potential problem with Berry's thinking is that everybody, even farmers, are tempted to grow in spite of what it might do to them and the community. Farmers, for example, borrow heavily, gobble up their neighbors' farms, and sell their water rights to cities, while they complain about everyone going out of business. So is it really farming that contributes to community or is it farming's strong work ethic?

Many people agree with Berry. However, it is not clear exactly what a family farm is. Browne et al. (1992) have a whole chapter entitled "Never Confuse Farming with Rural America" and another called "Never Base Decisions on the 'Average' Family Farm." Technically, family farms still produce almost all of this country's farm output. Fewer than 1 percent of farms are not owned by an individual, family, or partnership (Economic Research Service, n.d.). Nevertheless, not all of these farmers share agrarian values. Very few farms produce the majority of our food. On most farms, about 85 percent of the operator's income comes from off-farm sources. It is true that as the number of farms falls, farm sizes get larger. But other family farmers buy most farms. Therefore, big farms are usually successful family farmers, not corporations. The majority of farmers in the United States are part-time farmers; some are that way by choice, but many have off-farm jobs to make ends meet on the farm.

USDA considers a farm any establishment that sells $1,000 per year in agricultural products. Under this definition, three-quarters of all farms sell less than $50,000 of farm products per year and, on average, lose $3,000 per year (see Exhibit 3 in Chapter 4). Their $43,198 off-farm income in 1995 is comparable with the national household income of $44,938 in that same year (Economic Research Service, n.d.). The average net worth on these small farms is nearly a quarter-million dollars. Clearly, many "farms" in the United States are only hobby farms because they consistently lose money and are still worth so much. In the West, for example, working cattle ranches are being carved up into small ranchettes for vacation homes. Should we protect all small farmers, including these hobby farmers? If not, what fair criteria could be used to determine which of the 1.5 million small farmers are good for this country (as Berry and others describe) and which are not?

Why Are Farms Disappearing?

The reason farms are being lost in such great numbers is really quite simple. Farmers are just too productive. While the size of the farm sector may be small, it is highly productive. Only about 2 percent of U.S. workers are employed on farms, yet they feed the country and provide about 10 percent of our exports. In 1994, farmers spent 3 percent less on inputs to produce 2.5 times as much food value as they did in 1948.

Technology Growth

The reason farmers can produce "too much" is because of our phenomenal technology growth. Farmers in the United States have managed to produce on average 1.9 percent more each year than the year before, with the same inputs, for over 50 years. The average milk cow increased production 59 percent from 1975 to 1995. It now takes only seven weeks and eight pounds of grain to produce a broiler chicken. In the 1940s, the average American worked 30 minutes for every pound of chicken they bought; in 1995, it only took 4.5 minutes.

Foods Are Price and Income Inelastic

More people with more money should translate into more agricultural sales. Incomes have increased dramatically in the United States, but little of the extra income goes to eating more food. The population grew only 40 percent since 1948, which was far too little to consume the 2.5-fold increase in agricultural value. Export growth has helped tremendously. In less developed countries, people spend a higher percentage of their income on food, their populations grow faster, and their productivity growth rates are typically lower than in the United States, making them good customers.

The market keeps sending very strong signals to farmers, in the form of low prices, that they produce too much. The market demand for most foods is both price and income inelastic. In the United States the income elasticity of demand for food (the percent change in food purchases for a 1 percent increase in income) is only about 10 percent. That is, only about 10 percent of every new dollar is used for agricultural products. Therefore, higher consumer incomes in the United States have not helped farmers very much because people want to spend their money on other things. Likewise, prices are inelastic. For most agricultural products, producers would actually earn more revenue if they produced less— prices would rise more than enough to compensate for lost sales. Yet technology keeps pushing more products out on an already oversupplied market. Marketing orders and quota systems that restrict production by law are routinely used for milk, tobacco, almonds, and other crops to control production and increase farm earnings. A person cannot grow and sell tobacco, for example, without verifying that he or she owns a piece of the allowable quota.

Sometimes it seems as if agriculture is its own worst enemy. For example, we produce new products that make cows produce 10–15 percent more milk, while in the mid-1980s we paid producers to slaughter dairy cows because we had too much milk.

Americans spend only 11 percent of their income on food, and about 23 cents from every food dollar goes to the farmer. Therefore, only 2.5 cents from every food dollar makes its way to the farmers. We are spending our increased earnings on value-added services to make our lives more convenient, such as precut vegetables and pot roasts that take only ten minutes to cook. This creates a modernization crisis, as discussed in the next section. In the end, producers are driven out of production when fewer farmers are needed to produce the same amount of food.

The USDA National Commission on Small Farms released a plan in January 1998 with 146 recommendations about how to preserve small farms (1998). According to the report, the U.S. Department of Agriculture and other government agencies have fostered the growth of large farms and pushed small farms out. The report points out that small farms can be as efficient as large farms, and also that they provide many "hidden" benefits such as diversity of ownership, cropping systems, landscapes, biological organization, culture, and traditions. In addition, preserving small farms avoids monopolization of agriculture and a better environment and treatment of animals.

Characteristics and Farm Structure

Most farms in the country are small, family farms (USDA 1998). Very few of the farms are large, but these large farms are responsible for most of our agricultural output. Over half of all farms are in favorable financial health, but 45 percent of the small, noncommercial farms are financially vulnerable or have marginal incomes. Nearly 99 percent of producers are family operations or partnerships (Economic Research Service, n.d.). About 85 percent of these are small, noncommercial farms, accounting for about 20 percent of gross cash sales. The remaining 15 percent of farms are commercial farms that generate 30 times more sales revenue than noncommercial farms. The assets on commercial farms are 3 times that of noncommercial farms.

Overall, farm income is comparable with average income in the United States, but on average 89 percent of farmer's income comes from off the farm. Full-time farmers have four times more acres and eight times more income than farms where farming is not the principal occupation of the operator. And farmers who rent all or part of their land sell two to three times as much as those who own everything.

Farm Employment

A powerful argument used to mobilize concern about agriculture is the loss of jobs. Losing a farm or a farm job is a terrible thing for any individual and is a crisis at some level. However, workers released from agriculture are absorbed elsewhere in the economy to do other things. The economy is enriched because our food production is more efficient. We still have the same amount of food, but we have additional benefits that the released workforce provides, such as the benefits from computers, entertainment, and art.

Texas Commissioner of Agriculture Jim Hightower called people forced out of agriculture the waste product of the agricultural revolution (Castle 1995). Nevertheless, the U.S. economy would not have been modernized if agriculture had not been so productive. And our lives would probably not be as good either. Historically, in the United States, displaced laborers do get new jobs rather quickly. And when these "waste products" get new jobs, they produce a higher-valued product or service than they did in agriculture. During the 1980s, when the business world was shaken up, most people that lost their jobs found new ones within one year, and half found a new job within two months (Powers 1996).

Farmers are made worse off by productivity gains, but the rest of us are made better off. To understand this, you only have to look at other countries. The release of workers from the agricultural sector is the key to growth (Mills 1995). In poor countries, the majority of workers are employed in agriculture because they need to be in order to grow enough food to feed the population (just as we used to have to do in the United States). As the economy grows, food demand grows more slowly so people shift out of agriculture and into new sectors where products are in higher demand.

Farm Income

To survive, one has to make enough money to pay one's bills. Farming is a risky business with many ups and downs in the markets and production. In addition, farmers shoulder huge loans to produce their crops. Nevertheless, on most scales, farm income is not currently that low. In the 1930s, farm income was only about one-third that of the average in the United States. In the 1990s, however, farmers' net incomes are about the same as the U.S. average.

One way that farm advocates such as the American Farm Movement tried to prove that farmers' incomes were low was through parity pricing. Parity prices are based on the notion that farmers today should get the same relative prices as they did in the "Golden Age" of farming, 1910–1914. Parity measures the ratio of prices received for commodities compared to prices paid for inputs. Parity in 1992 was only 48 percent, apparently making farmers half as well off as they were in the Golden Age (Tweeten n.d.). However, prices paint only part of the economic picture. Farmers were about 3.6 times more productive in 1992. That is, they produced 3.6 times more commodity value per dollar of input on each acre. Therefore, they only needed to have 28 percent parity (1/3.6) to earn as much today as they did in 1910–1914. When adjusted for increased productivity, farm prices were 175 percent higher compared to input prices in the "Golden Age." This increase in productivity explains how farm output prices that are not very different from 10 or 20 years ago can support farmers when their input prices are substantially higher.

Wealth

Farm wealth is also very healthy compared with the rest of the country. On average, farmers have a net worth exceeding $350,000, compared with under $100,000 for an average citizen in the United States. (see Exhibit 3 in Chapter 4). The largest farms have an average net worth of over $2 million, which is to be expected. Surprisingly, small farms also have a very high net worth—an average of $245,000. Since these farms, which comprise three-quarters of all farms, also lose over $3,000 per year, one could deduce that most are hobby farms. How else could someone afford to lose money every year and at the same time build a net worth almost three times as high as the national average for Americans?

Rate of Return on Assets

Any business that invests money into buildings, land, and other durable assets loses the use of that money while it is tied up in the business. A profitable business should glean enough revenue from the business after paying all its expenses to earn a comparable rate of return to that which could have been earned if the money was put elsewhere, like the stock market or a bank. A study by Monke, Boehlje, and Pederson (1992) found that farm returns matched or beat nonfarm investments. Average annual returns to agriculture over the 1960–1988 period were 10.6 percent, compared to 10.4 in the stock market or 6.1 in government bonds.

Financial Vulnerability

USDA considers farms and ranches in a favorable financial position when they have a positive income and a debt/asset ratio less than 0.40. These profitable, low-leverage operations are able to retain earnings, putting them in a position to take advantage of investment and expansion opportunities.

Marginal income farmers are businesses that have *negative* incomes and a debt/asset ratio of 0.40 or less. These farms generally face an earnings problem, which could be overcome with increased borrowing or sales of assets, both of which convert equity to cash. Marginal solvency farms generate positive returns, despite higher debt service requirements. While not experiencing earnings difficulties at the present time, these farms are susceptible to economic changes that may erode incomes and prevent them from meeting future cash commitments. At current asset values, equity on these farms may be insufficient to serve as security for additional borrowing to meet short-run cash needs.

Finally, vulnerable businesses have both negative income and debt/asset ratios above 0.40. Many of these farms are highly leveraged and demonstrate income deficiencies that diminish the viability of their business operations. They do not generate sufficient income either to meet current expenses or to reduce existing indebtedness. The highly leveraged positions of these farms may have resulted from disproportionate reductions in asset values relative to the amount of outstanding liabilities, increased indebtedness to fund past expansion or cash-operating shortfalls, or a combination of these factors. Regardless of the evolution of financial circumstances leading to their current highly leveraged position, some of these farmers may be forced out of production.

The financial status of farms is always tenable, since it is a hard business fraught with risks. However, by and large, farmers are not in bad financial health. According to USDA estimates, only about 6 percent of farms are financially vulnerable. About half are in good financial health, and about 40 percent have problems with marginal income or marginal solvency.

Why Is Agriculture Important?

Another reason to support agriculture is because of its importance to the economy or to the health of rural communities. Many commodity groups and other advocacy groups claim huge amounts of employment and income are related to agriculture, suggesting that agriculture is a very important economic engine. The direct contribution, however, is probably very small. The whole food and fiber system in the United States employs 18 percent of our people and produces 15.7 percent of our income (Lipton and Edmondson 1993). However, the food and fiber "system" includes grocery sackers, waiters, and many others that most people don't associate with farming. The farming sector employs only 1.6 percent of the workforce and provides only 1.1 percent of the nation's income (see Exhibit 8 in Chapter 4).

The direct impact of agriculture on the U.S. economy may be less than 2 percent, but its total impact is much greater. Farmers help the economy in a direct way by hiring people and creating income. In an indirect way, farm business activity ripples through the rest of the economy, multiplying the direct impact on jobs and income. Firms that do business with farmers, such as input suppliers and marketing firms, also hire more laborers and create new income. And all these extra people with new jobs buy more cars and homes and go to the movies more, creating even more jobs and income.

It is a common misconception that the farm multiplier is 7, indicating that there is a $7 increase in national income for every dollar increase in the sales of farm products. This comes from Carl

Wilken, who in 1944 published a pamphlet called "A Prosperous Post War Era Is Possible." He showed that the average ratio between nominal national income and the value of farm sales was 7. That ratio in the 1980s was 22.88, and farm products surely do not generate $23 for every dollar sold. The actual multiplier for income and employment in agriculture is closer to 1.5 to 2.5 (Hoag, Fulton, and Hornbrook 1995). Every dollar earned in agriculture and every job provided therefore generates about one more dollar and one more job in some other sector of the economy.

Every dollar abroad generated by agriculture also helps. According to the USDA Economic Research Service, each export dollar generates another $1.40 in supporting economic activities. Therefore, agricultural exports generated $133 billion in total economic activity in 1997. Agricultural exports also supported about 1 million jobs. About one-third of these jobs were in rural areas. A little over one in five of them was on a farm.

Even with the multiplier effects, agriculture has a very small economic impact on the economy as a whole. The economic impacts are hardly large enough to justify government intervention in agriculture to protect jobs. But what about including how important farms are to rural communities? Of the 2,288 rural counties in America, containing 83 percent of the nation's land and 21 percent of its people (Economic Research Service 1995), only about one-third (556) are farm-dependent (receiving more than 20 percent of their income from farms). On average, only about one-third of nonmetro counties had above-average economic growth rates in the 1980s. About a quarter of these counties were retirement communities, 35 percent were rural trade centers, and 20 percent were manufacturing-dependent. Only 3 percent were farm-dependent. In other words, there was a 1-in-35 chance of having above-average growth if you lived in a farm-dependent county (Drabenstott and Smith 1995).

Few counties are farm dependent, most farmers get their income from off the farm, and farm-dependence is not highly correlated with rural economic success. It therefore appears unlikely that farms are the economic engine of most rural areas either. A rural area will likely be helped more by a manufacturing project or a retirement community than by agriculture. That is not to say that agriculture is not important, or that it is not critical in some counties.

Many people have concluded that the minuscule economic size of the farm sector makes it of little economic importance. However, agriculture's small size may prove just the opposite. Agriculture is a lot like a spark plug in a car engine. The engine powers a car, but not without a spark to get it going. As agriculture became more efficient, more people and resources were released to propel the economic engine of the U.S. economy. Currently, only 10 percent of our economic activities provide those things that are necessary for our biological or physiological survival (Powers 1996). The rest is devoted to attractive but discretionary phenomena. We have cheap and abundant food, plus a lot of other things that make our lives better. We would have less of these discretionary items if we had to spend more time producing food.

Abraham Maslow introduced a hierarchy of needs, which orders our needs from most to least important. Our first and most important needs are physiological. We cannot think much about love, work on our self-esteem, or even worry about our safety if we cannot eat, drink, and sleep. Therefore, agriculture can be thought of as the support upon which higher-order needs rest. Its size is inversely related to the amount of other benefits we receive in society. Consider the illustration in Figure 1. When agriculture is proportionately small, a person can devote a lot of effort to higher-order needs. If the agricultural fulcrum at the bottom of the figure was bigger, the top portion of the figure, which contains our other needs, would be smaller. A society that spends half of its time producing food would have a proportionately bigger agriculture, but it would also have less time and resoruces to devote to its higher-order needs.

Figure 1: Abraham Maslow Hierarchy of Needs

A small, productive agriculture has given the rest of society many benefits, but it has cost many farmers their livelihoods. We may need farms and ranches to preserve open space, to provide wildlife habitat, and to provide a place to nurture rural virtues. In some places, like the Netherlands and Finland, society has decided that they have enough benefits from a "small" and productive agriculture. These countries are creating programs to preserve historic farm qualities. In the United States, programs are springing up all over the country to preserve open spaces and farms and ranches for similar reasons. Perhaps the efficiency argument for farm growth has played itself out.

Crisis 2: Modernization

Modern Changes and the Industrialization of Agriculture

Agrarian values are starting to erode as people question large subsidies to agriculture, how animals are treated, whether farmers take good care of the environment, and whether farmers are different than anyone else. Increasingly, people are pushing old values out in favor of modernization, which has been changing tradition since this country declared its independence. However, modernization has hit crisis proportion in recent years because rapid changes in technology have displaced many traditional farming methods.

Figure 2: Technology Outpaces Culture

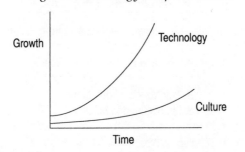

Sociologist Evan Vlachos (1998) notes that culture moves more slowly than technology. He suggests that society can face a "cultural shock" if technology changes faster than culture. Consider, for example, that some men are suing their ex-wives for fertilized eggs that were frozen, or that some women are having seven and even eight babies due to technologies meant to help infertile couples. These examples illustrate how technology has moved beyond culture. People have not had enough time to digest these issues and to decide what is right and wrong. In the case of modernization, there are many sources of concern, including genetic engineering of plants and animals, chemical use, animal confinement, and losing family farm values from vertical integration (see glossary).

Many people refer to this period of rapid modernization as industrialization. According to Boehlje (1996), industrialization of agriculture is "the application of modern industrial manufacturing, production, procurement, distribution, and coordination concepts to the food and industrial product chain."

In contrast to the old agriculture, the new agriculture moves toward: (adapted from Boehlje 1996)

- Manufacturing—Manufacturing food products instead of producing commodities, specialization, better coordination of phases of production, and therefore less waste all help combat risk (each stage knows what the other is doing or can take a loss if the other gains).

- Systems approach—Industrialization will match various stages more efficiently. Cost in any stage is not as critical as cost of overall product.

- Separation and realignment in the food chain—Each part of the process separates and specializes, there is more outsourcing, partnering (to take advantage of comparative advantage), and alliances.

- Negotiated coordination—Differentiation of products will replace spot markets. There will be better information flow and coordination rather than relying on spot markets.

- New kinds of risk—Some traditional risks are reduced. For example, some contracts will provide market security. Industrialization introduces many new risks, too. For example, concentration of food processing in factories can lead to food contamination disasters like the *E. coli* contamination that required Hudson Foods to recall 25 million pounds of hamburger in 1997. Concentration may also lead to more pollution. Putting all your eggs in one basket increases risk if, say, the contractor fails.

- Power and control—Information is power, and if one firm gains information at the beginning and end of the food distribution chain they get more power and control. Some people worry that, without goods trading in an open market, companies could end up controlling prices. However, marketing experts have found that very thin markets of less than 20 percent (80 percent of the commodity is contracted) can still provide accurate information about what is and is not a competitive price, where supply equals demand (Koontz 1999).

- Increased importance of information—Because information is power, it will become more important. Those who understand the increasingly complex food distribution system will be in the best position to take advantage of it. Also, as firms continue collecting their own information, it becomes harder to compete with them. A producer under contract relies on his or her contractor to provide information. Traditionally, information has been available to the general public through government agencies such as the Cooperative Extension Service.

Contract and Large-Scale Farming

One important outcome of industrialization is that more products are being processed under contract or for niche markets. In a contract farming arrangement, a producer controls his or her assets with compliance to strict rules from a company that agrees to purchase the end product. Often the company supplies many of the inputs so it can control quality. On the positive side, this arrangement creates security in a producer's income. However, it places his or her future in the hands of a corporate outsider.

Even though, overall, only about 12 percent of farmers sell their products through marketing or production contracts (Barr 1997), there has been a dramatic growth in contract farming in the last three decades for many industries. Over half of all vegetables, citrus, potatoes, sugar, seed crops, and milk are sold through contract. Effectively all broiler chickens grown for our kitchen tables are produced under contract. Cattle and hogs are less integrated, but concentration in the hog industry is looking a lot more like poultry farming every day. Over 80 percent of steer and heifer slaughter is controlled by just four packers.

Modernization has led to incorporation or to larger family farms and has caused farms to become part of an agribusiness complex in which much of the activity in preparing food and fiber occurs off the farm. Not even farmers agree about whether industrialization is good or bad for farming. The American Farm Bureau, for example, emerged as a modernizing force in the early part of this century. It imitated rather than attacked urban businesses. This modernization ideology favored viewing agriculture more like a business and less like a tradition.

Nearly everyone agrees that industrialization is a process of better market coordination aimed at getting products to consumers that better fit their preferences. Economist Steve Koontz (1999) and other agricultural marketing specialists have found that big companies replaced traditional agriculture because this coordination provided more value. For example, chicken prices have consistently fallen from 1960 to 1996, and quality and sales have risen. However, since 1960, beef prices dropped and then rose, and ranchers now sell less beef at a lower price. According to Koontz, the poultry industry simply did a better job providing higher quality at a lower price. Changes in consumer preferences for chicken over beef for health or any reason other than better value have probably been overstated.

The poultry industry is virtually 100 percent vertically integrated and controlled by only a few companies. The Tyson Food Company, for example, controls nearly half of all broiler chickens sold in America. The hog industry has followed suit. The number of hog farms fell 60 percent from 1985 to 1998 as small farms succumbed to large ones. Over 90 percent of those remaining sell less than 1,000 animals per year, and over one-third are contractually tied to corporate packers.

The beef industry is trying to avoid this trend toward corporate farming. Many efforts under way attempt to provide beef producers with the benefits of coordinated management without merging production, processing, and marketing into a single, vertically integrated company. For example, ranchers may decide to retain ownership and contract their feeding services rather than sell their animals to feedlots. This arrangement increases risks for the ranchers but provides an opportunity to earn greater profits by gaining more control over two separate stages of production. Another effort, called strategic alliances, forges cooperative agreements between two or more stages in the marketing channel (e.g., feeding and packing) that allow two or more separate producers to act as if they were vertically integrated. *BEEF* magazine published a handbook (Kniffen 1998) with details on 31 U.S. alliances. Some of them, such as the Certified Angus Beef program, have been very successful, raising prices for those producers who can meet the program's production and quality standards.

Community Costs of Industrialization: The Case of Hog Farms

What are the costs of industrialization? Is it worth it for beef producers to try so hard to avoid integration into giant corporations? Communities all across the country are in turmoil over just such a question. And nowhere is this question more prevalent than in large-scale hog farming.

Hog farms can be huge and produce as much waste as a city. One farm in southern Utah currently carries 260,000 hogs on any given day and employs 400 people. Obviously, somebody thinks these confined hog operations are beneficial. But many people feel they are costly to communities, too (Allison 1999; Cantrell, Perry, and Sturtz 1999). The waste alone is a concern to many people. Odor from concentrated lagoons can reduce property values and make people ill (Cantrell, Perry, and Sturtz 1999). Soil can be contaminated with dangerous heavy metals from land application of waste, and nitrogen and phosphorus can pollute water.

Out of concern over the potential negative impacts from large-scale concentrated hog farms, Thompson and Haskins (1998) looked at whether industrialization was necessary to get the benefits that corporate farms say they provide. They compared the contributions of four hog farm sizes to rural communities. The authors of this particular study wanted to show that many small farms can deliver as much benefit to the community as one big farm, so the benefit estimates are based on roughly 3,400 sows produced by the various-sized farms. Regardless of whether it was one big farm or many smaller farms, raising 3,400 sows employs about 20–30 people, with about a $700,000 to $1 million payroll. An extra person is also employed off the farm for each of these farm workers, bringing total employment created to 40–60 people. Estimated revenues to the local government are from about $25,000 to $30,000 per year. Thompson and Haskins showed, therefore, that several smaller farms can produce the same attractive benefits of a single large farm.

Costs and benefits are, of course, much broader than these economic impacts. Hoag and Fathel-Rahman (forthcoming 1999) summarize the results of large-scale confinement hog farms from several community studies. They looked at productivity, employment, health, taxes, community services, real estate value, and social implications. Employment, for example, increases in the short run by 7–25 jobs per 1,000 sows to accommodate building facilities, but drops to 14–16 in the long run. Each job pays about $14,000 per year. Larger firms pay higher wages and have better benefits, but they also have an extremely high turnover rate. Also, large farms tend to hire from outside the community. They hire one-third as many people per hog produced compared with independently owned, smaller producers (St. John 1999). Real estate prices have been shown both to go up due to the initial increased demand for jobs and down due to concerns related to odor. Social impacts are mixed. Large farms are more efficient, which helps meet the expected worldwide increase in demand for protein. Their workforce is also more culturally diverse. However, the costs of community services like hospitals and schools for company employees and their families are often higher than the taxes collected from the corporations. One county had to spend an extra $20,000 per year on gravel for roads for a 45,000-head hog farm. Also, larger firms have been accused of being less concerned about animal welfare and the environment.

Claims about corporate farms are controversial. For example, animal welfare may be diminished by the hogs' confinement, and the concentration of hogs can lead to environmental problems such as nitrate leaching into groundwater. However, some people argue that large-scale farming is better for both animals and the environment as larger organizations are better able to cope with such problems than are small farmers.

People that are concerned about industrialization would like society to help independent producers because, they assert, these producers are better for the community. The very process of industrialization suggests that small producers are less efficient. However large farms might just have more market power. Vertically integrated farms can lock smaller producers out of the market. A study in Nebraska predicted that if pork packers controlled 50 percent of production, they would pay 26 percent less for hogs purchased from independent producers (St. John 1999). On a single day in North Carolina, packers paid $51 per hundredweight to their own producers and only $39 per hundredweight to independent producers (St. John 1999). Of course, it might just be the case that contract growers locked in a better price. Regardless of whether small producers are less efficient, most opponents of corporate farming argue that small producers are better for the community.

Government Subsidies

One of the most contentious community issues is whether industrialization should be helped along by government subsidies. Nebraska Beef Ltd. in Omaha, for example, got between $24 million and $31 million in subsidies such as job, tax, and investment credits (Barlett and Steele 1998a). Much of the money was to stimulate good jobs, but the company has a 50 percent job-turnover rate per year and pays just $8 an hour to new employees, with a raise of 25 cents per hour every year they stay on the job. Archer Daniels Midland, the world's largest agricultural commodity firm, gets many subsidies. It earned $13.9 billion in revenues in 1997, but still took in $400 million that year in subsidies.

In the end, the question probably comes down simply to whether the economic benefits of large, corporate farms outweigh the perceived or actual community benefits of independent farms. And the answer to this question may vary for every farm, farmer, and location.

Biotechnology

Biotechnology is also a growing concern related to modernization. In a 1997 survey by the International Food Information Council (1995), two-thirds of the respondents expressed positive attitudes about the use of biotechnology. People were more supportive of manipulation for agricultural purposes, such as insect control, than for consumer reasons, such as taste. Nevertheless, many people remain very concerned about potentially devastating impacts related to biotechnology, such as introducing exotic species to the environment and increasing pest resistance.

Examples of genetic modification include controlled ripening in tomatoes, peas, and broccoli for better shipping quality; insect resistance in tomatoes, potatoes, corn, and apples; herbicide tolerance in soybeans, tomatoes, corn, and wheat that allow reduced use but more effective herbicides; and low-caffeine content in coffee beans for natural decaffeination. Corn and cotton now contain a gene from a soil bacterium called *Bacillus thuringiensis* (Bt) that makes it resistant to the European corn borer. The European corn borer damages millions of acres every year. Experiments show about a 95 percent reduction in damage, without the use of pesticides, and a 4–8 percent increase in yields (Carlson, Marra, and Hubbell 1997). Another product is Roundup-ready soybeans.

Roundup is a herbicide that kills weeds and crops on contact, but it is very effective and safe. By making soybeans resistant to Roundup, the product can be used in place of a variety of selective herbicides aimed at weeds only. Experiments show a reduction from $25 to $30 for conventional treatments to about $18 per acre with Roundup-ready soybeans.

Europeans are much more concerned about genetically modified crops (GMCs) than Americans are. This can affect the United States in two ways: by hurting exports and by influencing American consumers to avoid GMCs, too. By 1998, 25 percent of corn, 38 percent of soybeans, and 45 percent of cotton grown in the United States was genetically modified (Longman 1998). British tabloids have dubbed GMCs "Frankenfood." Companies could be in trouble if the public demands food labeling or "GMC-free" products since many companies don't know which of their raw products are GMCs and which are not.

There are potential risks from these "transgenic" crops. The products may speed or slow resistance in pests. The transgenic crops may also spread their genetic enhancements to other nontargeted crops with unknown effects, or become "weeds" themselves. The vine called kudzu, which was introduced for erosion control, has become a problem on many roadsides in the eastern United States. The difficulty we have killing kudzu is mindful of what can happen when new plants are introduced into the environment. In one case, Pioneer Hi-Bred International, Inc. introduced a new variety of corn that was vulnerable to gray leaf spot in the Midwest. They were blamed for an epidemic that claimed thousands of acres as it marched across Missouri, Iowa, Illinois, and Indiana. In addition, some people are worried about the toxins that these products may introduce to our food system. Environmentalists in the European Union decried Bt a mutant and have kept it from their markets.

However, there is also evidence that Bt will reduce microtoxins in corn such as aflatoxin, which is carcinogenic. Nevertheless, in June 1998, a coalition of scientists, interest groups, and religious groups filed suit against the Food and Drug Administration to stop the marketing of 36 transgenic crops. The group was concerned that the products are not labeled or tested thoroughly enough and that eating a carrot gene in a tomato, for example, might expose someone to allergies or violate their religious principles if they were unaware of the genetic enhancement. No settlement has been reached as yet.

Crisis 3: Feeding a Growing World

Food security is not a crisis in the United States. Chronic oversupply better characterizes our food situation. Nevertheless, things could change. Farm price and income supports began to be phased out in 1996, and the new market orientation has left buffer stocks highly unstable. Export demand is something everyone seems to want because it would bring higher farm prices. That is a good thing as long as exports only compete for our excess production. However, it is highly conceivable that export demand for U.S. farm products could escalate to a level in the future that threatens to significantly increase U.S. food prices. Most likely this would not create a crisis because we spend so little of our food dollar at the farm gate. An increase of 50 percent would only increase food prices by about 1.25 percent because the lion's share of food cost is not in the commodity but in the value-added component. In addition, we have had tremendous success improving yields with technology in the past. And, in a worst-case scenario, we could limit exports if we ever got into trouble, which is a lot better than having to find imports if we can't feed ourselves.

What about the rest of the world? Population is sure to increase. Can we feed everyone? Is there a looming catastrophe on the horizon? Globally, there are about 2,700 calories available per person per day in the food we currently produce. We feed almost twice as many people as we did 35 years ago and with a better diet. People in developing countries consume 30 percent more calories, including 50 percent more from animals, than three decades earlier. Yet, over 800 million people in the developing world don't get sufficient food to meet their needs. Food production increased 39 percent in the 1980s, but per capita production grew only 13 percent because of population growth. What will the future bring?

Future Supply and Demand of Food

Concern over the carrying capacity of the earth was expressed long ago. An English economist named Thomas Malthus in 1798 developed the notion that populations will outgrow food supply because population grows geometrically but food supply grows arithmetically (linearly). However, in the last half of this century, food production growth has outpaced population growth for most of the world. Thanks to people like Norman Borlaug, who won a

Nobel prize for his contribution to the Green Revolution (see Borlaug's biography in Chapter 3), we have been able to outpace food demand by matching crop needs to local environments so as to increase yields.

Nevertheless, many people around the world don't feel so lucky. A recent report from the Food and Agriculture Organization of the United Nations entitled "The State of Food and Agriculture 1998" estimated the number of chronically undernourished people in developing countries at 828 million between 1994 and 1996 (Web site). This is the first upward turn in over 20 years. A Food Security Assessment done by USDA in 1998 found that food security is falling in many low-income countries as the gaps between actual food consumption and minimum nutritional needs increase, and the gap is predicted to widen further over the next decade. The 1998 food gap in 66 low-income countries is 11 million tons, up from 8.5 million in 1997.

Luther Tweeten (1998) of the Ohio State University compiled various studies to look at future demand and supply of food. He used a linear growth function, which projected continued increases in crop productivity and population projections from three different sources. In 1995, the world's population was 5.6 billion people. Food demand growth from 1995 until world population peaks will be from 144 to 201 percent, depending on whose population growth figure is assumed. A low estimate of how many people will be in the world when population levels off is about 10.5 billion by 2084. On the high end, if we reach 11.3 billion by 2128, then demand will grow by 201 percent.

Demand for food grows both because people have more income and because there are more people. Tweeten predicts that demand will outstrip supply until about 2030. After that, our rapid technological growth rates actually reduce prices because supply grows more than demand. Tweeten's results are comforting because they show that a crisis is not inevitable. However, we must continue to find the yield increases he assumes and be able to curb and eventually halt population growth. In addition, technology growth may be too expensive to adopt in poor countries, and it may be too hard on the environment, so many people may suffer disproportionately more than others. Finally, some people contend that our current production relies too heavily on unsustainable levels of inputs, especially energy and water. If these resources become stressed, we may not be able to feed even the people that are already here today.

Losing Farmland

Losing farmland or water will reduce food security because the world will have a smaller stock of natural resources to use for production. Erosion, salinization, and exhaustion of water sources could threaten sustainability. Soil erosion is the single most serious cause of degradation on arable land (Kindall and Pimentel 1994). Losses around the world range from 20 to 300 tons per acre per year. Also, according to Kindall and Pimentel, the Worldwatch Institute estimates that soil erosion has caused farmers to abandon 1,063 million acres of arable land worldwide in the last 40 years. Finally, Kindall and Pimentel point out that irrigated acreage has doubled since the turn of the century, making the world rely more heavily on water for high yields. We rely on more pesticides and fertilizers, too. About 16 percent of the world's cropland is under irrigation, but this land contributes one-third of crop production. Current salinization rates are causing the loss of 1 percent of irrigated cropland per year. At this rate, half of all irrigated land will be lost by the year 2050. And farmers are expanding acreage to offset these losses, which threatens the environment. Less than half of the world's land area is suitable for agriculture and grazing. This could be expanded by one-third, but the quality of new land would be marginal compared to current land.

Avery (1998) counters that agriculture dominates land use throughout the world. Cities occupy only 1.4 percent, which is estimated to climb only to 4 percent in 2030. Farmland occupies a steady one-third of the world's land. Yield must increase two- to threefold to meet future demands when our population is doubled. Therefore, we have no choice but to rely on technology. Avery contends that expanding land use would be an environmental disaster, compared with other high-yield technologies like agrichemicals and genetic engineering.

The China Wave

Lester Brown brought this potential food shortage crisis to the world's attention in his 1995 book, *Who Will Feed China? Wake-Up Call for a Small Planet*. Brown considers 1990 the end of a 40-year economic era and the beginning of a new environmental era. Basically, the economic era has extracted all the growth in food it can, and the environmental era will impose corrections on us. This, he predicts, will threaten our sustainability.

China is in trouble, according to Brown, due to another half-billion citizens, shrinking cropland base, spreading water scarcity, and the need to raise cropland productivity. Nearly 82 million Chinese in rural areas find it difficult to satisfy their water needs. More than 300 Chinese cities are short of water and 100 of them are very short. He compares the rapid industrialization of China to Japan and Taiwan, which were also densely populated before industrializing. The cost of developing in those countries came in the form of heavy reductions in high-quality agricultural lands. In Japan, for example, grain production has fallen 32 percent from its peak in 1960, and the country relies more on imports. The grain area in China fell 1.4 percent per year in the early 1990s. However, their output increased fourfold from 1950 to 1990, and China now leads the United States in total grain production. Income growth rates in excess of 10 percent, coupled with adding another half billion people, will put tremendous pressure on already stretched resources.

Many people have countered Brown's claims. China's own economists, for example, disagree. Rozelle, Huang, and Rosegrant (1996) and the Organization for Economic Cooperation and Development (OECD) argue that Brown ignored adjustments that Chinese farmers and the government will inevitably make, and that he was overly pessimistic in many of his estimates (such as productivity growth rates). They predict with various assumptions that China will level out as a net grain importer at 43 million metric tons by 2020, which is hardly enough to swamp or even to dominate world markets (Brown predicted 216 million metric tons by 2030). In fact, China is number one in the world's production of swine, poultry, and horses; second in sheep and goats; and fourth in cattle. OECD points out that China may reverse recent reductions in agricultural investments and therefore raise growth rates if it experiences the kind of price increases in world markets described by Brown.

The Role of Technology

The head of the Consultative Group on International Agricultural Research (CGIAR) stated that there is still a huge gap between what can be produced and what is produced. Rice production, for example, averaged just 3.5 metric tons per hectare in developing countries in 1994 but has a biological maximum of 15 metric tons per hectare. The world therefore has the capacity to feed many more people if farmers worldwide can access the technology. The world could feed twice as many people as we do now just by getting all countries' yields up to the 6–7 tons currently achieved in high-yielding countries. India, for example, feeds twice as many people as Africa on only 13 percent of its surface area. The world could feed almost five times as many people if every country grew the biological maximum.

There will probably be about two times as many people in the world in the next 50 years, and that will stretch current production systems. Increased output can be met by more efficient technologies. Creating more economic freedom for women and taking better care of the environment (reducing salinity and desertification, for example) will also help. When women, or any other group of people, are held back through religion or culture, society is less prosperous. The same is true when environmental degradation is ignored. Most experts don't expect biotechnology to match the kind of increases the world saw with the Green Revolution. However, biotechnology is uncertain and things can change in a hurry.

Crisis 4: Safe Food and Drinking Water

One of the more recent crises in agriculture is food and water safety. Unfortunately, there have been situations where careless agricultural practices or food handling have resulted in illness or death. There have also been cases where unsubstantiated and untrue rumors about food safety have hurt agricultural sales. Advances in our ability to detect chemicals in food and water and evidence that food and water are not always safe have heightened concerns. Nevertheless, Americans rely increasingly on industry to preprocess their foods, consequently transferring control of food safety to other people—farmers, ranchers, and food handlers. This increasing lack of control raises concerns for many people.

Food and water safety is a crisis to consumers because they want to be safe. It is a crisis to farmers, ranchers, and food handlers because keeping food safe can be very costly. Not keeping food safe can be even more costly, so agriculture is taking the issue seriously.

Food Safety

There are many things in or on our food that may be unsafe. Some are natural, and humans introduce others, such as pesticides. Illness from foodborne pathogens is by far the most pressing problem. There have been several outbreaks of illness involving a variety of foods. In 1997, the Hudson Foods plant in Columbus, Nebraska, recalled 25 million pounds of ground beef contaminated with *E. coli* (see Chapter 8 for a description of the different pathogens). Other foods with outbreaks in the 1990s include cantaloupe, ice cream, raspberries, eggs, apple juice, strawberries, and oysters (*Newsweek* 1997). As many as 1,000 people were confirmed to suffer in some of these outbreaks, and 4 people died in one incident.

Another widely publicized food safety problem was "mad cow disease." Bovine spongiform encephalopathy (BSE), also called mad cow disease, is a degenerative neurological disease in cattle. A 1995 outbreak in England caused worldwide concern that it could cause a variant of a rare brain condition in humans known as Creutzfeldt-Jakob disease (CJD). In addition to allegedly killing up to 30 or more people, the epidemic in England reduced beef industry profits by 25 percent. USDA has not found BSE in cattle in the United States, but has banned imports of live animals where BSE is a known problem. There has not been a definitive link made between BSE and CJD. CJD occurs in about one in a million people including those who live where BSE has not been found, and in vegetarians and meat-eaters alike.

A related disorder that has been found in the United States is Chronic Wasting Disease (CWD). CWD is a mad cow–like spongiform found in deer and elk in the western United States. No one has become sick yet, but it is not known whether hunters are at risk or whether the disease can be transferred to cattle.

Food Safety Costs

Buzby and Roberts (1996) studied the impacts of seven of the major foodborne illnesses in the United States: *E. coli, Salmonella, Listeria monocytogenes, Staphylococcus aureus, Campylobacter, Clostridium perfringens,* and *Toxoplasma gondii*. They found that between 3.3 and 12.3 million people become ill by one of these pathogens each year and as many as 3,900 people die (see Exhibit 17 in Chapter 4). These totals include only the 7 pathogens they studied. There is no information for the up to 40 other pathogens thought to cause foodborne illnesses.

We all take risks when we think the benefits outweigh the costs. We drive cars, smoke cigarettes, and take jobs with higher risks because they pay more. The benefits of low-cost food are easy to observe. Some of the risk-related costs of food-production methods are straightforward to estimate as well, such as the cost of hospital stays or lost wages when someone becomes ill from food or water. But how does one value an early death? One approach is to estimate the future earnings that a person would have made in their lifetime had they not died prematurely. This method, called the Human Capital approach, was developed by Landefeld and Seskin in 1982 (Crutchfield et al. 1997). Another method is to study how much money people already accept for risky behavior. This hedonic approach, developed in 1993 by Viscusi, analyzes the labor market to determine the wage required to get people to take on risks (Crutchfield et al. 1997). Viscusi analyzed 24 high-paying, high-risk occupations, such as working on a skyscraper or being a firefighter. He found that the market would have to pay from $3 million to $7 million (in 1990 dollars) to induce enough workers to take on jobs where there was a probability of one extra person dying. The Consumer Product Safety Commission uses his estimates and places a $5 million price tag per life lost. In addition, the U.S. Environmental Protection Agency and Food and Drug Administration used Viscusi's $5 million figure.

Using these two approaches, Buzby and Roberts report a total cost from foodborne illness of between $6.5 billion and $34.9 billion every year. They report that this figure is low due to the impacts that they could not measure, both for the pathogens they reviewed and the ones with no information. While they could not caputre all costs, the study that Buzby and Roberts participated in was very thorough. Variables they considered include human illness costs such as hospital visits, lost wages, and costs related to pain and suffering, industry costs such as reduced productivity in livestock and costs to prevent the diseases, and government costs such as regulation and treatment costs when there is an outbreak.

Water Safety

Also of concern are waterborne illnesses such as the protozoan parasites *Cryptosporidium parvum* and *Giardia lamblia*. EPA predicts that up to 460,000 cases of waterborne illnesses occur per year. These organisms produce oocytes that are excreted by a host animal, and if they make it into water and then into the human gastrointestinal tract they can release sporozoites, which can cause severe diarrhea. Several outbreaks have been linked to livestock. The most publicized was a *Cryptosporidium* outbreak in Milwaukee, Wisconsin, in 1993. An estimated 400,000 people had watery diarrhea (Mackenzie et al. 1994). It is impossible to be sure where the outbreak came from, but possible sources include livestock in the area, slaughterhouses, and human sewage.

Discovery of nitrates and pesticides in America's water supply in the 1970s and 1980s dispelled the view that soil buffered and purified applications of fertilizers, pesticides, and other agricultural chemicals. The Safe Drinking Water Act updates passed in 1996 require states to identify sources of contamination. In 1997, the U.S. Geological Survey reported that at least one pesticide was found in every stream they sampled and about half the groundwater they sampled in 20 major U.S. watersheds (Smith and Ribaudo 1998). A 1992 study by the EPA sampled over 560 public drinking water wells. This study found that 14 million people served by community water systems (CWS) wells are exposed to at least one pesticide, although rarely above levels considered unsafe for humans. It also found that nitrate was the most frequently detected chemical, present in more than half of the CWS wells and 60 percent of rural domestic wells. About 85 million people were exposed and 3 million drank water that was above maximum contaminant recommendations (ten parts per million). Nitrogen occurs naturally in groundwater but can be elevated by nitrogen fertilizers and livestock wastes.

Pesticides

Public concern over pesticide use has caused producers great concern. One Midwest farmer, Will Erwin (1995), says farmers are becoming more and more uncomfortable about real and perceived environmental hazards. Continuous news stories about DDT, the ozone layer, pesticide risks, and biotechnology build fear about unreasonable regulation and even entrapment. Erwin believes many farmers are also uncomfortable with agricultural leaders who take extreme antienvironmental positions. Farmers want facts and moderate views between extremes.

According to the Food Marketing Institute (FMI), there are 10,000 different insects, 1,800 weeds, 160 bacteria, 250 viruses, and 8,000 fungi, which together destroy 30 percent of the nation's crops worth $20 billion each year (Food Marketing Institute 1998). There are about 21,000 pesticide products containing 875 active ingredients registered in the United States. Agriculture accounts for 71 percent of pesticide use. Only 200 active ingredients account for 98 percent of pesticides applied to agricultural products. In 1988, EPA listed 66 pesticide compounds as possible carcinogens. Estimates of the number of malignancies associated with pesticides in food vary from as few as 8 per year to more than 21,000. The higher estimate is derived from the theory that about 1.5 percent of the 1.36 million cancer cases diagnosed in 1996 were related to pesticides (FMI 1998). The World Health Organization (1990) estimates that a minimum of 3 million acute cases of pesticide poisoning and 20,000 deaths occur worldwide every year. Farm workers who handle and apply pesticides may be at an even greater risk.

Although pesticides pose risks to humans, nature produces its own toxins, too. Arsenic is found in fruits, vegetables, meats, and seafood at levels of less than 0.5 parts per million. The average adult consumes about 0.9 milligrams per day with no apparent ill effect. Plants must defend themselves against insects and weeds. Some plants produce their own herbicides, known as allelopathic substances. They are secreted from plant roots and inhibit growth of other plants. Rye, for example, planted prior to a corn crop, can inhibit weed growth without the use of pesticides. Other toxins that protect plants against herbivores, pests, and diseases are alkaloids, glycosides, phenolics, and toxic amino acids (Cheeke 1998). The fungus *Aspergillus flavus* produces aflatoxin, one of the primary natural toxins in livestock feeds and linked to liver cancer in humans. Aflatoxin is naturally carcinogenic, and is found in corn, soybeans, and peanuts.

Bruce Ames has reported in numerous publications (e.g., Ames and Gold 1997) that 99.99 percent of dietary pesticides are natural. The remainder are from synthetic pesticides. Americans ingest roughly 5,000 to 10,000 different natural pesticides, and about 1,500 milligrams of natural pesticides per person per day, which is well over 10,000 times more than they consume in synthetic chemicals, which average about 0.09 milligrams per person per day. Ames and colleagues developed the HERP index (human exposure/rodent potency) to rank carcinogenic chemicals. HERP rankings put human cancer risks in terms comparable to cancer studies in rodents. A person who consumes a given amount every day over a lifetime—one cup of apple juice, for example—of a substance with a HERP score of 100 percent would ingest a dose that caused tumors in 50 percent of rodents in a test group. A HERP ranking of 50 percent would give half the dose that led to tumors in 50 percent of the rodents. These are only ranks and may not be good indicators of actual risk. However, their major finding is that risks from both synthetic compounds and natural ones rank relatively low (see Exhibit 19 in Chapter 4).

There are some criticisms of the Ames HERP approach (Environmental Working Group 1998). However, the larger body of science supports Ames. Studies show that roughly 20 percent of synthetic pesticides are capable of causing cancer when fed daily to laboratory animals at high levels over a lifetime. According to the American Medical Association, however, there is no scientific evidence supporting a link between the proper application of pesticides and any adverse health effects in *humans* (FMI 1998). A 20-member panel of the National Resource Council, an arm of the National Academy of Sciences, suggests that diets too rich in calories and fats pose a far greater risk of cancer than pesticide residues and food additives. The February 1996 report also concurs that "chemicals that occur naturally in foods may pose a greater risk of causing cancer than the residues of synthetic pesticides that people consume in their diets. In fact, the great majority of individual toxic chemicals found in food, whether naturally occurring or synthetic, occurs at levels far too low to have any adverse effects on health."

Societal Concerns

A 1995 report by the Council for Agricultural Science and Technology (van Ravenswaay) concluded through surveys that the public believes that insects, diseases, and other pests need to be controlled, but that there are alternatives that are just as effective and no more costly than pesticides. The author concluded that it is unlikely that one pesticide standard will please everybody. She also concluded that the public is willing to pay more for less pesticide exposure, but it is uncertain whether the premium is sufficient to cover the costs of restricting use. What then can the government do to provide society with a reasonable level of safety?

What Is the Appropriate Role for Government?

The government can do many things that will help make our food safe. It can monitor our food, conduct research, and pass laws to provide safeguards. The FDA, for example, monitors food for pesticide residues to protect consumers. It tests over 10,000 domestic and imported food items each year. In 1995, 99 percent of domestic samples and 97 percent of imported samples contained no illegal residues, and no residue was detected on about two-thirds of the samples. A state monitoring program for ten states found 0.8 percent had significant residue levels. A USDA study in 1995 found less than 4 percent of samples carried illegal residues (Food Marketing Institute 1998). However, many people have criticized government estimates of food safety where it comes to residue levels. Groth, Benbrook, and Lutz (1999) concluded that many popular fruits and vegetables, such as peaches, pears, and spinach, have pesticide residue levels that violate the law and that impose risk on people who eat them.

In another example of government regulation, the U.S. EPA sets drinking water standards for many chemical contaminants that appear in drinking water. The two most common forms are maximum contaminant levels (MCLs) and health advisory levels (HALs). MCLs are enforceable by law, while HALs are not. Both are calculated to assure negligible risks of adverse health effects when compared to other risks in our everyday lives.

Whatever the government does, it can't please everyone. Setting risk standards too high might bankrupt agriculture (Jaenicke 1997); setting them too low might result in environmental or human casualties. Socially acceptable risk is not zero tolerance. We take risks every day when the outcome of the risk improves our lives. How much is too much risk, though? One often suggested criterion is that an unacceptable risk is big enough that the government should worry about it, but small enough that an individual does not worry about it. Avery (1995) argues that EPA regularly overstates pesticide exposure risks by a factor of one hundred. Bruce Ames in his various writings supports this claim. EPA uses theoretical maximum residue, while the FDA, for example, uses dietary intake. While some people argue that government methods allow intake levels that are still too high, others, like Avery, think allowable levels are set way too low. Government standards are based on assumptions that farmers spray the maximum amount, residues are not washed off or do not degrade appreciably, and that people consume ridiculous amounts. Avery (1998) attributes the rise in cancer to living longer, smoking, fatty diets, alcohol, and sunning ourselves, not pesticides.

In some ways, our fear of risk in food is not proportional to other areas of our lives. Every day, people undertake activities with risks that are as high as or higher than the risk standards for food. For example, riding a bike for 10 minutes equals the same risk limit set by our food safety requirements. That is, you would have a one-in-a-million chance of dying on your bike ride. Flying for 1,000 miles, riding 43 minutes on a school bus, living two days in New York or Boston, and having one chest x-ray taken also lead to risk levels that would cause those activities to be banned if they were governed by the same requirements set for food safety (see Exhibit 22 in Chapter 4).

People are willing to pay to protect themselves, either through taxes or by directly paying a producer. Willingness-to-pay studies find that households would pay from $100 to $1,000 per year to protect themselves from agricultural chemicals. A survey in four areas of the United States found that people were willing to pay between $45 and $60 per household per month for a water filter that reduced nitrates to safe levels (Crutchfield, Cooper, and Hellerstein 1995). However, the respondents were willing to pay only about 3 percent more ($1.61) to completely eliminate nitrates from their tap water. Studies show that individuals place a value of between $0.5 million and $9 million on a statistical life (Fernandez-Cornejo, Jans, and Smith 1999). Based on this estimate, the government appears to be balancing the benefits of agricultural activities against our willingness to accept risk. For example, one study estimated that between 1975 and 1989 the Environmental Protection Agency implied, through their decisions about whether to cancel or continue to allow the marketing of certain pesticides, a tradeoff of $9 million per cancer case avoided. That is, the use of a pesticide would be canceled unless the cancellation resulted in more than a $9 million loss to farmers (Fernandez-Cornejo, Jans, and Smith 1999).

Irradiation

Irradiation can kill foodborne pathogens. Irradiation is a process that exposes food to ionizing radiation, which injures or kills harmful bacteria. There are three types permitted: gamma rays, high-energy electrons, and x-rays. A dose of 2.5 to 3.0 kilograys will control or reduce *Salmonella, E. coli,* and *Vibrio vulnificus,* but higher doses would be needed to control viruses and spores such as *Clostridium botulinum.* Irradiation costs from four to eight cents per pound for larger meatpackers. One study estimated that if 25 percent of the 7 billion pounds of ground beef consumed in 1995 were irradiated, the savings in medical costs and productivity losses to salmonellosis and *E. coli* would have been $56.4–$137.7 million (Morrison, Buzby, and Lin 1997). This level of irradiation would cost the beef industry $28 million. Market research indicates that consumers are willing to buy irradiated meat, once they are informed about the benefits. Sixty percent in one survey said they would pay ten cents more per pound (Morrison, Buzby, and Lin 1997). Disadvantages include a possible discoloration and odor, and possible slight reductions in the vitamins A, C, E, and B.

Hazard Analysis and Critical Control Point Program

The most recent government response to concerns about food safety in the meat industry was to create the Hazard Analysis and Critical Control Point (HACCP) program. HACCP is a system of process control that can be used to prevent hazards to food by control, reduction, and prevention of pathogens. Effective January 1998, about 75 percent of the nation's raw meat and poultry products are in an HACCP system. One might think that the government would inspect meat after it is processed. However, HACCP emphasizes contamination prevention by building in safety controls throughout the production process (Becker 1992).

Crutchfield et al. (1997) studied the costs and benefits of HACCP. They estimate that HACCP will cost from $1.1 to $2.3 billion per year. They estimate benefits from $1.9 to $171.8 billion per year. Their lowest estimate assumes that only 20 percent of pathogens would be controlled by HACCP. Given that almost every estimate places the effectiveness of HACCP closer to 90 percent, the costs appear to be clearly justified by the benefits. (See Exhibit 23 in Chapter 4.)

Organic Certification

Sometimes the government can help by just providing information. In 1990, Congress required USDA to create an organic certification program, which is still not finalized as of the middle of 1999. Organic certification allows concerned consumers to choose foods that have not had pesticides or synthetic fertilizers applied so they can make their own choice not to consume synthetic compounds, rather than relying on the government to set a standard that they agree with. In 1995, the USDA established six principles that are key to organic farm management (Duram 1998): (1) protect the environment, (2) replenish and maintain long-term soil fertility, (3) maintain diversity, (4) recycle materials and resources, (5) provide attentive care to farm animals, and (6) maintain the integrity and nutritional value of organic foods.

Studies indicate anywhere from a 0 percent to 400 percent price premium for organic foods (Dobbs 1998). A typical premium might be in the 50 percent neighborhood. One research group indicates that 12,000 farms employ organic methods, although only about one-third of those are certified by an independent private organization. Another group suggests that 5–7 percent of U.S. farms practice organic methods. A 1994 USDA study found that only 0.34 percent, or 1.13 million acres, were certified organic. While production is small, sales are growing fast. Since 1989, annual sales have grown at a rate of 20 percent, and totaled $3.5 billion in 1996.

Food labeled organic will not necessarily protect a person from foodborne diseases such as *E. coli* and *Salmonella*. Odwalla brand juices (not an organic but a "natural" product) had an *E. coli* outbreak in its apple juice; now they pasteurize. The organic-friendly University of California at Berkeley *Wellness Letter* (1995) stated that "it is hard to say" whether organic products are safer. Furthermore, "there's no evidence, one way or the other, about their effect on consumer health." They go on to suggest that organic foods still have better value because "it's a vote for a kind of agriculture that replenishes the soil and protects the water supply as well as those who work in the fields."

The Alar Scare

A 1989 report by the Natural Resources Defense Council (NRDC) declared Alar, a growth regulator used mainly on apples, a cancer-causing agent. Although government and health experts disputed NRDC's allegations, public uncertainty over the safety of apples continued for several months, and Alar was subsequently withdrawn from the market voluntarily by its manufacturer. Upon further testing, EPA concluded several years later that the health risks associated with Alar were greatly exaggerated. Nevertheless, apple sales plummeted $100 million. A series of "veggie" laws—which also apply to livestock—were implemented in at least 16 states as a result of the NRDC Alar affair. These laws empower agriculture to recover damages if disparaging remarks cause losses. However, the first serious legal test of these laws failed when, in 1998, Texas Cattle Feeders lost their lawsuit against Oprah Winfrey based on veggie libel laws (see Exhibit 21 in Chapter 4).

Crisis 5: Stewardship and the Environment

An important ideological rudder, if you will, that guides the way many people view environmental management is whether they consider themselves to be anthropocentric or biocentric. Anthropocentric, or "human centered," means that resources matter only to the extent that people care about them. Biocentric, on the other hand, means "biology centered." The latter viewpoint suggests that natural resources have some intrinsic or innate value. All creatures are created equal and therefore humans should not subdue nature, but live in harmony with it.

These two seemingly opposing positions are not really inconsistent at all and unnecessarily lead to conflicts about how nature should be managed (or left alone). The biocentric ideology suggests that environmental concerns lie outside the realm of humans. This is implausible because people can only interact with others in human terms. Biocentric thinking is therefore anthropocentric as well. *Everything* we do is for our own self-interest, including when we decide to put the interests of nature above our own. The science of economics, which is clearly anthropocentric, does not suggest that the social organization of goods and services concerns only business and commerce. It is legitimate to demand biocentric goods and services, such as a better environment or the good of another species.

It would be equally narrow to suggest that the anthropocentric viewpoint considers only market or utilitarian goods. A tree, for example, can provide more than just lumber. It can provide shade, a place for songbirds to congregate, and beauty. The economic market recognizes many of these other values. A home with a nice tree in front will command a higher price than the same house without a tree. Additionally, people donate money simply to protect a species for its own sake, demonstrating monetary value for nonmarket items.

This distinction is important because people often incorrectly pit the environment against market goods. Every day, people make choices for one market good over another, given their limited economic budgets. Likewise, we make decisions about our natural resources that trade a little of one environmental service for another or exchange an environmental service for a market good. By making a donation to save whales, for example, a person is trading the market good he would have bought with the money for protecting the nonmarket value of whales. Why then should people pit the environment against the economy? People compare tradeoffs for scarce resources, regardless of whether someone wants to cut a tree down to build a log cabin or to protect it for songbirds. All goods and services have value to somebody.

Economists often use money to compare apples to oranges, but that doesn't mean that economists think goods sold in the market are the only things of value. Goods have use and nonuse value. Nonuse values include the option to use a resource in the future and the value a person gets by knowing something exists or that it can be handed down to the next generation. Use values can be consumptive or nonconsumptive. A consumptive use would be hunting deer, and a nonconsumptive use would be simply to take its picture. Many goods have value but no market price.

Environmental Impacts from Agriculture

One study (Costanza et al. 1997) estimated that the total value of the world's ecological system was $16–$54 trillion in 1994. The value in the United States alone was estimated at $33 trillion. These are phenomenal estimates considering that the world gross national product was only $18 trillion in 1994.

Costanza's study has been widely criticized for being too extreme, but it highlights a good point. The only way that the economic value of the world's resources could be greater than our gross national product is to count the market value of nonmarket goods. For example, a concession stand in Yosemite National Park may sell $250,000 worth of hats, T-shirts, and novelties, but the value of these souvenirs rests on the economic value that attracts people to the park in the first place.

Overall, economists have a tough time estimating nonmarket values. Smith (1992) estimated the total cost of agricultural impacts on the environment to be almost 13 cents for every dollar sold. He calculated that soil erosion costs about 4.5 cents per dollar, because erosion makes it necessary to dredge for navigation and reduces recreational uses, fishing, reservoir storage, and flood protection. Wetland damage costs about 2 cents. And groundwater contamination costs society about 6 cents for every dollar of output sold. Of course, people derive a lot of value out of our cheap and abundant food, too. So it's not only the farmers that are getting benefits from environmental degradation. The question is how much degradation is too much.

Production Practices and the Environment

Farmers and ranchers have responded to the call for improved stewardship. Although water quality, wetlands conservation, and wildlife protection could still be better, they have all improved (Economic Research Service 1997). These improvements have come in no small part because farmers and ranchers have taken the responsibility to adopt production practices that are friendlier to the environment. Generally, nutrient use on farms in the United States has leveled off since 1980 and pesticide use has declined (Aspelin 1997). There are three important reasons why nutrient and pesticide levels are falling: (1) industry has made pesticides and other agricultural chemicals safer and more effective, (2) educators have concentrated on teaching the best management practices that match agricultural needs with environmental concerns, and (3) precision farming uses technologies such as global positioning systems and modifications to equipment to place inputs only where they are most needed.

Many producers are also adopting soil conservation practices. About two-thirds of crop producers use some form of conservation tillage. In addition, beginning in 1985, any farmer with highly erodible land had to file a conservation plan before he or she could collect price and income support or get loans from government agencies. In their plans, farmers had to detail how they would produce crops without excessive soil erosion. Conservation plans were submitted on more than 139 million acres, over a third of all cropland in the United States.

Besides saving soil and reducing the use of agricultural chemicals, farmers around the country are engaging in hundreds of different kinds of environmentally friendly practices. They are protecting wildlife habitats, diverting agricultural runoff away from lakes and streams, using production systems that treat animals with more care, and providing a more scenic countryside. After the great dust bowl disasters of the 1930s, producers showed that they will adopt soil conservation measures when they are made aware of the consequences of their actions. The relatively new emphasis being placed on other problems, such as nitrate in groundwater, appears to be having a great effect, too—farmers have adopted precision farming, better management practices, and other conservation measures. However, it will take time for these management practices to become fully integrated into modern farming systems.

Water Quality

The U.S. Environmental Protection Agency (EPA) reports that agriculture is the single biggest polluter of surface waters in the United States (Economic Research Service 1997). For example, 72 percent of the river miles that EPA found impaired (polluted to a level that they do not function like clean water) were damaged by nonpoint source (indirect discharge) pollution such as runoff from agriculture. A little over half of the problems in lakes were from agriculture. While there were very few wells polluted with pesticides, over half were polluted by nitrogen (nitrogen also occurs naturally). All but a handful of states have to issue warnings from time to time that fish might be contaminated by agricultural sources. Finally, cropland erosion creates sediment in lakes and rivers, which cost more than $2 billion in 1989, for example (Economic Research Service 1997).

There are many more exotic water-quality problems from agriculture, too. For example, a hypoxic (low in dissolved oxygen) area 40 percent the size of Lake Erie appeared in the Gulf of Mexico off the coast of Louisiana (Hewitt 1998). The nutrient-enriched waters from the Mississippi are thought to be the primary cause of this "dead zone," where fish and shrimp populations have been diminished. The U.S. Geological Survey estimates that 90 percent of the nitrogen being delivered originates from nonpoint sources, predominantly from agriculture. In addition, over 40 pesticides and products from pesticides have been found in the Mississippi River (Hewitt 1998). On average, concentration levels in the Mississippi were low, but occasionally they rose above EPA standards in the summer months. The combined impact of pesticides, soil, nutrients, and even channelization of freshwater is largely unknown, but could be catastrophic.

Wetlands

There was a time when the government gave tax breaks to investors that would drain wetlands and convert them to cropland. That was before we learned that wetlands preserve water quality, provide habitat for fish and wildlife, prevent erosion, reduce flood damage, and are appreciated for their aesthetic beauty. (See Exhibit 32 in Chapter 4.) Even though society values these contributions, it is extremely difficult for an individual landowner to be able to collect any financial compensation for providing the resource. Between first settlement in the U.S. and 1954, an average of 800,000 acres of wetland were converted to cropland per year (Heimlich et al. 1998). We now convert only about one-tenth that amount each year, but we have lost over half of the wetlands in the lower 48 states. Heimlich et al. found that the total of all wetland values combined can exceed $100,000 per acre. They found average wetland values of $6,132 for market goods, such as fish, shellfish, and fur-bearing animals; $94,400 for nonmarket goods, such as the willingness of people who fish, hunt, and recreate on land and water affected by wetlands to pay to protect their uses; and $34,871 for ecological functions, such as amenity and cultural value.

Soil Conservation

Soil erosion has been the number one environmental concern of farmers since Hugh Hammond Bennett (see Chapter 3) established the Soil Conservation Service (now called the Natural Resource Conservation Service) in the 1930s. The huge dust storms and economic devastation of the dust bowl forever ingrained the importance of soil on the minds of farmers.

Even though farmers worked hard to reduce erosion rates, conservation was difficult until 1985. The Food Security Act of 1985 launched a major new commitment by the federal government to reduce incentives that prevented the widespread adoption of conservation practices. Price and income support programs, for example, had encouraged monocultures and intensive cultivation. As a result of these efforts, conservation needs have been cut dramatically. Erosion rates have dropped steadily since these perverse incentives were reduced and new conservation programs were created. In 1982, the average erosion rate was 4.1 tons/acre/year. That number fell to 3.7 in 1987 and 3.1 in 1997. Over 15 years, erosion has decreased by 24 percent (Economic Research Service 1997).

Erosion is a problem because it reduces the ability to produce crops and because sediment that leaves the farm leads to pollution. Pierre Crosson (1997), an economist with Resources for the Future, estimated that erosion would reduce agricultural productivity 3 to 10 percent per century. The World Watch Institute estimated that since the 1950s, soil erosion caused farmers to abandon land equal to about one-third of our current cropped acreage.

In the mid-1980s, scientists started to realize that the costs of pollution from soil erosion are much greater than the on-site productivity losses. As shown earlier, Smith (1992) found that 4.5 cents of every dollar of output sold was due to the off-site damages from erosion.

Air Quality

Air quality is a relatively new concern for agriculture. Agriculture pollutes the air and is also impacted by air pollution. Besides tailpipe emissions from farm equipment, cultivating stirs up dust that blows into cities. The EPA recently tightened air-quality standards such that particulate matter from blowing dust could bring a lot of new attention to agriculture in counties that are finding it difficult to meet government standards. The degree of impact on agriculture from these regulation changes is not known at this time.

Agriculture could also be affected by global warming. Scientists predict that the average world temperature could rise a few degrees, perhaps 1.5 to 4.5 degrees Celsius, from greenhouse gases such as carbon dioxide. No one really knows whether climate change will have dramatic impacts on agriculture, or if it will have any impact at all. Precipitation patterns could change, creating hardships, but carbon dioxide can help plants grow better, too. Three studies that simulate global impacts are summarized in Exhibit 33. Two of the three studies predict that crop yields would actually go up, and on average there would be no impact on the world crop economy. However, a closer inspection reveals that all three studies show that the developing nations will suffer, which most likely would increase the wealth gap that already exists worldwide.

Wildlife

Farms and ranches provide food and habitat for 75 percent of the nation's wildlife. Their impacts on wildlife are highly variable. Some species, such as deer and raccoons, do better, and some, such as pronghorn and prairie dogs, do worse. Many species that are hunted have increased due to the economic incentive to protect their habitat. Colorado ranchers for example charge $2,000 to $10,000 per hunter to allow people to hunt elk on their property. However, Wilcove et al. (1998) estimate that agriculture is responsible for 38 percent of the habitat destruction or degradation that harms federally listed endangered species. Livestock grazing is responsible for 22 percent of these losses. Invertebrates, amphibians, insects, arachnids, crustaceans, and mussels are affected the most. Mammals are affected the least. Loomis and White (1996) estimated the economic value of endangered species to be from $6 a year per household for a striped shiner minnow to $70 for a northern spotted owl (see Exhibit 34 in Chapter 4).

One very good example is salmon recovery in the Pacific Northwest. Agriculture in the Pacific Northwest totals 5 percent of all production in the United States. In 1992, the total value of agricultural products in this productive region was over $9 billion, including $5.4 billion for crops and $3.7 billion for livestock. A key to the success of this region is irrigation, which represents over half of all cropland. This water comes in part from an elaborate system of dams and reservoirs along the Columbia and Snake Rivers. Besides irrigation water, this system provides electricity through 150 hydroelectric dams and recreation such as boating and fishing.

Unfortunately, this impressive accomplishment for people has come at a grave cost for the salmon that use these rivers to spawn. Most people are aware that adult salmon swimming upstream must maneuver a labyrinth of fish ladders to get to their spawning beds. Three dams alone eliminated such migrations for one-third of the salmon runs. However, most people are not aware that the juvenile fish are finding it highly difficult to make it to the ocean. Salmon and steelhead populations have fallen to about 20 percent of their historic level. And all but 2 percent are produced in a hatchery.

Salmon have a huge social importance, but this importance can also be measured in dollars and cents. One study (Aillery et al. 1996) compared the costs and benefits of various proposals to help juvenile salmon make it to the ocean more easily. They looked at three basic methods to help these fish: reservoir "drawdown," which reduces the size of slack waters in large reservoirs making them easier to cross; "flow augmentation," which increases flow velocity in rivers; and a cadre of investments in irrigation infrastructure, such as screens to keep salmon out of irrigation channels. Their study found that improving flow would provide between $58,000 and $463,000 from commercial catch, plus about the same range again for recreational fishing. However, recreational boating losses of $8 to $28 million would swamp those benefits. Agricultural profits would fall by $4 to $30 million per year.

Avery (1998) argues that the best way to save wildlife is to use high-tech farming because it plows fewer acres. This is an interesting observation because it involves supporting intensive agriculture, which uses more agrichemicals. Which is the lessor evil? Certainly, intensive agriculture has environmental benefits. Avery estimates that organic farming, for example, would require the conversion of 20–30 million square miles worldwide (52–78 million square kilometers) of wildlife habitat by the time the world population peaks at 9 billion in 2040. That land area is bigger than North and South America, Europe, and Australia combined. If dairy producers in New York produced milk like they did in 1960, they would need 2 million more acres. Ontario chicken producers would need more than a million acres if they all went to free-range methods. Opposing the high costs of extensive farming are the environmental costs of intensive agricultur, as discussed earlier.

Social Reactions

There is great division in society about how to address environmental problems, primarily because we can't agree how much degradation is acceptable in order to produce market goods. Many farmers feel there are too many regulations. A 1990 report by the U.S. EPA estimated that for all businesses and governments, $115 billion is spent annually to meet environmental regulations. This figure will climb to 2–3 percent of the gross national product (GNP) by the year 2000. It took 65 years from 1898 to put ten environmental laws on the books. Since 1965, there have been ten put on the books every 4 years (Kushner 1991). Environmental spending in the United States totaled around 1.5 percent of GNP in 1990 and was greater than that of West Germany, Japan, Netherlands, United Kingdom, Austria, France, and Norway.

Some people want to save the environment through technology. Tweeten and Forster (1998) estimate that crop output in 1990 would have required 734 million acres if produced with 1950's technology. That's 393 million more acres than the 341 million harvested in 1991. They estimate that expanding our farm base would require moving onto fragile lands that could be three times more erodible, with as much as six times more erosion, than current land that is in production.

Many private organizations have spent a great deal of time and effort on environmental issues in agriculture. The Sierra Club's policy on agriculture can be found at their Web site, for example. The Sierra Club and groups like it have fought for local, state, and federal policies as well as helping farmers find funds to improve their land.

Of course, the most substantial source of assistance comes from the government. Expenditures on resource conservation programs affecting agriculture totaled nearly $7.5 billion in 1996. These programs cover many agencies, such as the USDA, the EPA, the Army Corps of Engineers, and the U.S. Department of the Interior. However, no single program has been as extensive as the Conservation Reserve Program.

The Conservation Reserve Program (CRP) was initiated as part of the Food Security Act of 1985. The program was established to temporarily retire up to 45 million acres (about 10 percent) of highly erodible cropland. Farmers that enrolled received assistance for establishing a conservation cover of grass or trees and an annual rental payment, around $45 per acre for most farmers.

Overall, the program enrolled 35.5 million acres of highly erodible land plus another half million acres of other sensitive land. The program cost $19.5 billion, but reduced erosion by 700 million tons per year. (See Exhibit 38 in Chapter 4.) The nonmarket values of resources like land have been discussed above. In the case of the CRP, these values may have paid for the program (Hoag forthcoming 1999). Setting aside cropland in vegetative cover saved soil productivity, improved surface water quality, increased small-game hunting, and provided a whopping $4 billion in nonconsumptive wildlife uses, such as bird-watching. The net benefits of this very expensive program were estimated to be anywhere between a slight loss and $8.1 billion. (See Exhibit 39 in Chapter 4.)

A companion program with the CRP was Conservation Compliance. This program assured that farmers who received government price and income supports, and others, used conservation on any of their highly erodible fields. USDA estimated that this program provided over $2 of benefits for every $1 it cost (Economic Research Service 1997).

Crisis 6: Urbanization and Land Use

In many ways, it is a good thing when a family can move out of the city and back to the urban fringe where they might appreciate a simpler lifestyle. It is good for the rural areas where they move, too, because it brings income and neighbors and helps keep the community viable. However, too much of a good thing can become bad. Urbanization converts farmland into developments, possibly threatening our future ability to produce food, to say nothing about the loss of countless other amenities that farms and ranches provide.

Urbanization has been a steady problem in the United States for a couple of decades, but recently it has risen to a crisis level. People want to save land while there is still some left. In some places, like Howard County, Maryland, near Baltimore, the community has raised millions of dollars to preserve the little open space that is left there. However, it is too late to be very effective because the community is already overcrowded and congested.

Farmland Conversion

On a grand scale, urbanization is not seriously threatening our productivity. Developed land accounts for only 3 percent of all land and, even with high growth rates, will only grow to 4 percent in 50 years. Sorensen, Greene, and Russ (1997) estimate that in a worst-case scenario, we would have to feed 50 percent more people in 50 years with 13 percent less high-quality land. We could farm more land, but it would be marginal, which might lead to environmental problems. Also, we would diminish our trade opportunities. We might not need to worry anyway. If productivity grows by historical rates of 1.9 percent annually, in 50 years we will produce nearly 150 percent more food on every acre, more than offsetting the lost acreage. Even at half that productivity growth rate, we would produce over 50 percent more food.

Urbanization on a local level affects communities in a way not captured in productivity. An analysis by the American Farmland Trust (AFT) (Sorensen, Greene, and Russ 1997) found that every state lost some prime or unique farmland to urbanization and development. The state with the most prime farmland (37 million acres), Texas, lost more of it than any other state—487,000 acres—during 1982–1992. That loss alone accounts for 11.5 percent of all decreased farmland acreage in the United States. Rounding out the top five states converting the most prime farmland are North Carolina, Ohio, Georgia, and Louisiana. Total prime or unique farmland converted during 1982–1992 was nearly 14 million acres, which is about 1.5 percent of all farmland or about 3 percent of total cropland (farmland, ranges, forests, and crop-related buildings and roads) in the United States (see Exhibit 41 in Chapter 4).

Overall, the study by AFT concluded that the United States is "squandering" its best-quality land, limiting our future options to deal with social, economic, food, and environmental problems. Even if the there were no food problems, AFT points out that the loss of other amenities provided by these lands, such as open space and wildlife habitat, are reason enough to cause concern.

Causes of Urban Sprawl

The reasons for metro and urban growth have been well documented (Mills 1995). In poor societies, most people work in agriculture because productivity is so low. When productivity rises, incomes rise, and an increasingly smaller share of income is used for food, leaving the rest for other endeavors. In the early stages of growth, people move into manufacturing. Later, people move into service industries like advertising and shipping.

Metropolitan areas attract most of the growth in population, industry, and development because of their proximity to consumers and producers, which makes it cheaper and easier to exchange goods and services. A surprising amount of "agriculture" goes on in or very near the city, although even at high levels of agricultural production, other businesses provide the bulk of the total income of urban areas. For example, Jefferson County in Colorado has the highest agribusiness income in the state, but derives only 3.9 percent of its own income from agribusiness.

The direction of migration of people and businesses has historically been from the rural areas to the cities. Over the last 150 years, the population in rural areas has declined from over 90 percent to about one-quarter of the U.S. population. In recent years, however, urbanization is starting to move people and some of their businesses in the other direction. About 20 percent of metropolitan workers live in rural areas and commute to their jobs. Mills (1995) concludes that a small number of these people serve agriculture by connecting the countryside to the city (for example, the trucking industry). However, Mills reasons that the bulk are moving out to take advantage of opportunities that only rural areas can offer—oftentimes because new technologies such as telecommuting allow them to live farther from work. In rural areas, wage rates are lower, housing costs less, taxes are lower, and many people enjoy the quiet lifestyle.

Key factors that cause the conversion of undeveloped land were identified by Daniels and Bowers (1997). The first, of course, is population growth. However, the government has played a part, too. A better infrastructure, including roads and telecommunications, makes living in the country much more comfortable, drawing more people out of the cities to take advantage of the lower taxes, more open space, and other amenities the country has to offer.

Impacts on Society

One of the biggest costs of urbanization is increased conflicts between city and country folk who do not always share the same values. (See Crisis 7 beginning on page 54 for a detailed discussion of this issue.) However, measuring the costs and benefits of losing our open spaces is more traditionally based on economic criteria.

Fiscal analysis measures the impact of population growth in terms of net public service costs for roads, schools, and the like. Many studies show that unplanned growth and development may be costing local governments more than it brings in. Surprisingly, residential development generally leads to a higher net fiscal deficit than farm uses. Nonresidential development actually generates a fiscal surplus. An American Farmland Trust study, for example, showed residential costs were $1.11 per dollar of revenue raised compared to only $0.31 for farm and forest. AFT reports that studies in more than 40 communities over the past decade confirm that owners of farm, forest, and open lands pay more in local tax revenues than it costs to provide services, and that residential land uses cost more than they bring in.

A study in Colorado about the benefits of ranch open space shows how much people really do value open space and farms and ranches (Rosenberger, Walsh, and McKean 1996). Visitors and residents of a mountain valley said that next to the natural environmental amenities, ranch open spaces with barns, corrals, and haystacks, and the cowboy culture itself, made living in the country most enjoyable. Nearly 30 percent said that preserving ranch open space was most important for protecting it for private enterprise and the rural economy. Over 10 percent were willing to pay $400 per year to preserve open space, and another 60 percent were willing to pay between $30 and $400.

Policy Tools

According to AFT, there are at least five reasons to save farmland:

To ensure food security
To create economic opportunity
To invest in community infrastructure
To protect natural resources
To sustain the quality of our lives

The people in the United States seem to agree that preservation is important. Nationwide, there are over 1,100 private land trusts that have preserving open space as their primary mission (Hocker 1996). In January 1999, President Clinton proposed spending $1 billion to preserve open space and to fight urban sprawl.

There are many new and innovative ways being developed to protect farmland. The AFT has a variety of useful fact sheets and publications and an excellent help service at their Web site.

Many land-protection tools have been devised at the state and local level (see Exhibit 44 in Chapter 4). Some states are making it possible to create agricultural enterprise zones where farmers and ranchers can feel less threatened by urbanization. For example, in an agricultural district farmers are partially protected from nuisance suits brought against them because their animal pens smell or because they create dust when cultivating their fields.

The Nature Conservancy is a leader in the purchase of conservation easements. Usually in cooperation with government, they pay a landowner the difference between what they could earn for development and what they could earn by keeping the land open. Many people like the idea enough to donate their land into easements. Other state actions are right-to-farm laws (which are similar to agricultural districts), growth management laws that control timing and phasing of growth, and tax relief.

Local governments can help through zoning or transfer of development rights. Zoning that eliminates the opportunity to develop is unpopular because the owner is not compensated for his or her loss. However, new ideas like cluster zoning are creating new and more popular opportunities. Colorado, for example, has a minimum 35-acre size for development in most counties. A developer could put 10 houses on a 350-acre parcel. Cluster developing might allow 12 houses if they are located together and a large open space is preserved, rather than having ten people each having 35 acres of open space. This reduces fragmentation, preserving more of the open space amenities. Finally, the impact of the federal government should not be ignored. A single law, like the Endangered Species Act, can significantly alter the playing field.

Crisis 7: Country and Urban Conflicts

Finally, crisis is brewing in rural America as people with urban backgrounds take up residence in the countryside. One farm woman with whom I spoke started home-schooling her children because the local school adopted too many "city" ways as her neighborhood became urbanized. A team of concerned country representatives in Colorado even put together a booklet for their new neighbors about how to be a good rural citizen (Jones n.d.). It contains many sections, including one called "A Few Things You Need to Know to Get Along in the Country" and another called "Respect: The Code of the West."

This crisis is partly about outsiders having something to say about the way agricultural people do things. For a long time, farmers and ranchers were left alone to make decisions about the vast resources under their control. They were stewards of the land. We assumed they did a good job. Now some people think farmers are more villainous than virtuous. They believe the government should step in and protect the land so that farmers do not pollute it and to keep an eye on how animals are treated. While this must be very frustrating for those unaccustomed to such scrutiny, it's probably a good thing that the rest of society takes an interest in agriculture. Benefits flow from their involvement, too. Many people who look over farmers' shoulders are also willing to generously support programs to keep farmers in business.

The following sections discuss the important role that property rights play in directing change, then examine three areas where conflicts are evident: animal welfare, public lands, and water.

Property Rights

Property rights are a sacred and important principle that has guided growth in the United States. Property rights include the right to exclude others from your property, to occupy and derive beneficial use, and to convey and bequeath your property to others. Rights are important because they dictate what can and cannot occur on property, which determines its flow of goods and services. Where property begins and ends is not clear. For example, irrigation helps farmers grow crops but also affects in-stream flow and the species that live in streams in national forests. Who owns the rights to the water? If the farmer has the right to continue irrigating without concern for the forest, he alters the flow of goods and services on his farm and in the forest. If the U.S. Forest Service has a right to maintain in-stream flow, benefits from the forest are increased, but the farmer's returns are reduced.

When conflicts occur, the government sometimes steps in to solve them. The U.S. Constitution contains language to assure that the government does not violate private rights in an effort to capture public benefits. According to the Fifth Amendment of the United States Constitution:

> No person shall be . . . deprived of life, liberty, or property, without due process of law; nor shall private property be taken for public use, without just compensation.

The Fourteenth Amendment of the United States Constitution states:

> No State shall . . . deprive any person of life, liberty, or property, without due process of law; nor deny to any person within its jurisdiction the equal protection of the laws.

There are two types of public intervention. The first, called "eminent domain," concerns cases where compensation is required. For example, the government can take your land away from you for a highway, but it has to pay just compensation. The second is called "police power." Rather than physically taking property, the government takes away value through restrictions on use, such as easements or zoning requirements. Police power is typically used for activities that may be injurious to the health, morals, and safety of the community. Laws against prostitution are often cited as an example of police power. *Compensation is not required* under police power for two reasons. First, nuisance or noxious use may be harmful to neighbors or the general public. Second, all property must be regulated to a certain extent, and the government could not afford to compensate every loss.

Many people think that the government has to compensate a citizen when there is a "taking" of private value, citing the Fifth Amendment, but they forget about police power. Recently the courts have been leaning increasingly toward requiring compensation. However, there are no absolute rules. Some courts have ruled in favor of those who want to limit uses on private property, and others have ruled against those seeking to limit use.

Pease (1998) summarized several court rulings about property-rights takings (see Exhibit 45 in Chapter 4). He found that, generally, a government action goes too far and becomes a taking if there is no economic use of the property left after the action, or the action is not linked to a valid public purpose. For example, a rancher might be restricted to keep animals out of a stream where fish are endangered because there is still economic use on the ranch and saving endangered fish is a legitimate public concern. However, the government might have gone too far if it totally eliminated the ability of the rancher to raise cattle, or if it required that the public have access to see the endangered fish.

The conflict over rights is well demonstrated by the "wise-use" movement. The basic tenet of wise use is that "conservation is the wise use of resources," which is a statement originating from

Gifford Pinchot, noted conservationist and first chief of the U.S. Forest Service. People who subscribe to this movement believe that the original meaning of "conservation" has become corrupted to mean "preservation without use." Conservation should mean responsible use (Arnold 1996). Many environmental groups scorn the wise-use movement, believing that it is a radical antigovernment group using wise use as an excuse to destroy the environment. Additionally, they believe that it is backed not by grass roots but by corporations.

Right-to-Farm Laws

One of the tools used to protect farmland and open spaces is right-to-farm laws. The subject is included here because it demonstrates the battle over rights between property owners and society. Right-to-farm (RTF) laws or declarations are designed to protect farmers from nuisance suits and antifarming ordinances. (See Exhibit 46 in Chapter 4 for an example of one county's RTF policy.)

According to Janie Hipp of the University of Arkansas National Agricultural Law Center (1998), most of the RTF laws require that a farm or ranch had to be in existence before plaintiffs began to have problems and that the area around the farm changed and caused a conflict, instead of a change on the farm. An operation can't maintain its rights if it expands or adopts new technologies that impose new threats to its existing neighbors. In other words, they protect farmers from nuisance suits if they were there first. The major criticism of RTF laws is that they are vague. Also, RTFs take away the rights of others, such as a neighbor who has to deal with odors from livestock, to have their day in court.

In the *Bormann vs. Board of Supervisors in and for Kossuth County Iowa* case in 1998, the Iowa Supreme Court held the Iowa right-to-farm law unconstitutional. The Iowa RTF statute stated:

> A farm or farm operation located in an agricultural area shall not be found to be a nuisance regardless of the established date of operation or expansion of the agricultural activities of the farm or farm operation (Hipp 1998, p. 5).

Nevertheless, the court found the legislation unconstitutional because the legislature had exceeded its authority "by authorizing the use of property in such a way as to infringe on the rights of others by allowing the creation of a nuisance without the payment of just compensation" (Hipp 1998). Basically, Iowa declared RTF a taking on the part of the agricultural district from the surrounding areas because it took away from the rights of neighbors to enjoy their property free of nuisance from farmers.

Animal Welfare

Concerns about animal welfare have been around for a long time, but more contact between farmers and city dwellers has heightened concern to a crisis level in some circumstances. The conflict in animal welfare occurs because of both value differences and ignorance. Many farmers and ranchers contend that people who don't have to work with animals don't really understand what needs to be done and what is and is not proper treatment. Beyond such conflicts, however, are serious fundamental differences in the way people think animals should be treated. In general, an "animal rights" philosophy is more extreme than an "animal welfare" philosophy. Welfare is humane treatment, but animal rights contend that animals have equal rights to humans (see Exhibit 47 in Chapter 4).

The beef industry's response to animal rights, for example, is largely to point out how important slaughtering cattle is to society. Besides being an important source of food and protein, raising cattle utilizes grasses that can't be used for anything else (although recreationists would dispute this assertion), recycles many food by-products like sugar beet pulp and potato skins, and provides pharmaceutical products such as collagen and insulin. The animal industry is also quick to point out the economic damage and terrorism inflicted on it by the radical component of the animal-rights movement. According to the Department of Justice, damages have been as high as $4.5 million for a single incident (Center for Defense of Free Enterprise n.d.).

Public Lands

Public land is another area where agricultural and nontraditional values clash. Millions of acres of public land are controlled by agencies like the Forest Service and the Bureau of Land Management (BLM). In the western states, the federal government owns as much as 89 percent of the land. It is the onerous task of the government to direct use on these lands to satisfy multiple and competing interests, like timber, habitat, grazing, and recreation.

Historically, ranchers have had easy access to much of this land for grazing. People who want the land used for other purposes, such as recreation or wildlife protection, increasingly raise concerns, however. Criticisms over grazing include that it diminishes biodiversity, deteriorates range condition, erodes soil, leads to desertification, and depletes watersheds and riparian areas, among many others (Laycock 1996). A scientific review by the Council of Agricultural Science and Technology concluded that while degradation is occurring in localized areas, overall livestock-grazing methods are not degrading public lands. In addition, the loss of grazing permits would likely lead ranchers to sell to developers, which would threaten important winter range for big game and other wildlife.

Water

Another place where nonfarmers are questioning farm use is water. About 80 percent of the water used in the West is used by agriculture. Many environmental problems have been linked to agricultural use. For example, Moore, Mulville, and Weinberg (1996) calculate that the endangerment of 50 species of endangered fish in the western United States are linked to agricultural activity, and 235 counties contain irrigated production that relies on water from rivers with these fish.

In 1902, Congress passed the Reclamation Act to build dams and irrigation projects to supply water to "small" farmers. In 1998, water goes mostly to big farmers, such as a 22,000-acre cotton farm, a Japanese drugmaker, and a multimillionaire potato farmer (Barlett and Steele 1998b). Cheap water from the federal government to farmers costs the taxpayers about $1 billion per year through a complex web of subsidies. The Reclamation Reform Act of 1982 pledged that large farmers would pay the full cost and limited subsidies to farms under 960 acres.

One example showing that farmers have resolved some of their differences with society can be found on the John Day River in Oregon (Western Water Policy Review Advisory Commission 1998). Irrigation on two farms along the John Day River in Oregon was threatening salmon runs. A cooperative project between landowners and government restructured their diversion systems, producing a net benefit of $16,500 (see Exhibit 54 in Chapter 4).

Coping with Change and Transition

People involved in agriculture have three choices when confronted by change:

quit and walk away from the problem,
cope with the change, or
cultivate the change

Even if a change is a good thing, it might still be painful. In this situation, it is helpful to learn how to cope with the change. In his best-selling book, *Managing Transitions: Making the Most of Change*, William Bridges says, "it isn't the changes that do you in, it's the transitions." Change, Bridges explains, is not the same as transition. Change puts a person in a new situation. You might have a new job, live in a new place, or start using irrigation on your crops for the first time. Transition is the psychological process people go through to come to terms with their new situation. How well do you accept the change, and how well do you cope with it? Change is from the outside, and transition is internal.

According to Bridges, transition has three steps. First, a person has to let go of the past—transition begins with an ending. After letting go, a person enters a neutral zone—between the old reality and the new beginning. The old way is gone but the new does not yet feel comfortable. Third is the new beginning. For example, a man who accepts a new job in a different city will say good-bye to his friends but let go of his past in anticipation of his new life. For a while after the change of job and location, he will feel uncomfortable and miss his old life, while at the same time appreciating his new life. Then, in stage three, he will become comfortable in his new life and begin to concentrate on the present.

Perhaps, in addition to addressing how agriculture is changing, some attention should also be paid to helping producers learn to cope with change. Bridges suggests that people in transition need to respect or observe the end of the old ways through celebrations honoring traditions, for example, in order to move on. He also suggests that the "neutral zone" be made as comfortable as possible so that people don't try to rush through it faster than is needed. Even producers and others who push for change need to cope with the transition.

Cultivating Change—Government and Society

Maybe society, and farmers in particular, should not accept that all changes are good. Nor should farmers or rural communities cope with changes that are not right for them. "A trend is not destiny. . . . Those that live by the crystal ball are bound to eat ground glass," says Evan Vlachos (1998). We could fight change. However, change can be both good as well as bad. Therefore, another option is to *cultivate change;* make it what we want it to be. Encourage what we want and discourage what we do not want.

Cultivating change requires careful monitoring of winners and losers, research about the impacts of change, and effective, enforceable policy. This must be a community effort because individual interests are usually more shortsighted than society's. Most people would consider it shortsighted, for example, to put a cold drink concession at the bottom of the Grand Canyon, even though there would be plenty of businesses willing to profit from thirsty hikers that make the long trek to the bottom. However, individual rights must also be protected so that the collective does not unfairly benefit at their expense either. America is already embroiled in a battle over individual versus collective rights (e.g., gun control, abortion rights, and land use). While these battles are difficult for everyone, the stakes are high, so fighting for good solutions is probably worthwhile.

What American agriculture needs is a shared vision for the future. Extra stress is put upon farmers and ranchers when they are constantly defending themselves no matter what they do. For example, right-to-farm laws can help establish an understanding about what most of society agrees is a reasonable relationship between agriculture and its urban neighbors. Shared visions, like the RTF laws, also need to be made in the areas of the environment, animal rights, public lands, public waters, biotechnology, food safety, and rural development, to name a few. A shared vision about what most people think is right and wrong could be very helpful, even if it is not enforced by laws or policies.

While there probably is no single shared vision for agriculture, there are a few directions that I offer here:

1. **Ending Entitlements:** We are most likely seeing the end of the era of entitlements. The agrarian ideology will not be strong enough to win financial support in the future when so many other equally deserving groups are being told "no more entitlements." Therefore, if government supports are needed, they will have to be earned on other bases. Supports will be given in times of crises, when prices are so low that livelihoods are severely threatened. However, on a more permanent basis, people will only support agriculture when they believe it helps themselves. For example, people may

pay farmers to produce in a more environmentally or
animal-friendly manner (sometimes called "green payments"). Perhaps people will want to save the "small farm"
because it prevents food monopolies or because overproduction provides food security.

2. **Increased Risk:** With the Federal Agriculture Improvement
   and Reform Act of 1996 phasing out commodity price-and-
   income support programs, there will be more financial risk
   to farmers. Other factors that increase risk include higher
   borrowing to pay for more technically complicated production practices, international competition, and environmental
   liability.

3. **Increased Outsider Input:** People outside agriculture will
   have a greater say in how products are produced. In the
   past, producers were the caretakers of their land and other
   resources. People were satisfied to get cheap, high-quality
   food. In the future, people will want to be sure animals are
   being treated well, that chemicals do not end up on food or
   in the water, and will want access to "public" goods on the
   farm like wildlife or public access. This could mean heavy
   government intervention, such as mandatory inspections.
   Increased marketing of environment- or animal-friendly
   products can slow intervention.

4. **Loss of Voluntary Programs:** Voluntary programs will be
   replaced with regulations or fines. Until recently, farmers
   were asked to voluntarily change their practices when
   problems occurred. And when they would not or could not,
   subsidies were offered to help. Society will increasingly shift
   to regulations, fines, or cross-compliance programs that limit
   subsidies to only those that comply with socially set standards.

References

Aillery, Marcel, et al. *Salmon Recovery in the Pacific Northwest: Agricultural
and Other Economic Effects.* Report No. 727. Washington, DC: U.S. Department of Agriculture, Economic Research Service, 1996. 72 pp.

Allison, Roger. "The Corporate-Controlled Factory System Is Inherently
Flawed." *In Motion Magazine*, http://www.Inmotionmagazine.com, 1999.

Ames, B., and L. Gold. "Environmental Pollution, Pesticides, and the Prevention of Cancer: Misconceptions." *FASEB Journal* 11 (1997): 1041–1052.

Arnold, R. *A Wolf in the Garden: The Land Rights Movement and the New Environmental Debate.* Edited by Philip Brick and R. McGreggor Cawley. Lanham, MD: Rowman & Littlefield Publishers, 1996.

Aspelin, A. *Pesticides Industry Sales and Usage: 1994 and 1995 Market Estimates.* Report No. 733-R-97-002. Washington, DC: U.S. Environmental Protection Agency, Office of Prevention, Pesticides and Toxic Substances, 1997.

Associated Press. "Deaths Linked to Mad Cow Disease Up in 1998." March 2, 1999.

Avery, D. *Saving the Planet with Pesticides and Plastic.* Indianapolis, IN: Hudson Institute, 1995. 432 pp.

———. "The Promise of High-Yield Agriculture." *Forum for Applied Research and Public Policy* 13 (1998): 70–76.

Barlett, D., and J. Steele. "Corporate Welfare." *Time* 152 (November 9, 1998a): 38–53.

———. "Fantasy Islands and Other Perfectly Legal Ways That Big Companies Manage to Avoid Billions in Federal Taxes." *Time* 152 (November 16, 1998b): 79–93.

Barlett, Peggy F. *American Dreams, Rural Realities: Family Farms in Crisis.* Chapel Hill, NC: University of North Carolina Press, 1993. 305 pp.

Barr, T. "Industrialization of Agriculture or a Realignment of the Food and Agricultural System?" In *Increasing Understanding of Public Problems and Policies* (1997 National Public Policy Education Conference Proceedings), 88–104. Washington, DC: Farm Foundation, 1997.

Becker, Geoffrey. "HACCP: Prescription for Safer Food or Smokescreen for Deregulation?" *CHOICES* 7 (Second quarter, 1992): 28–29.

Beneke, R. "Progress Comes Dressed in Strange Clothing." *CHOICES* 13 (First quarter, 1998): 42–44.

Berry, W. "A Defense of the Family Farm." Chap. 27 in *Is There a Moral Obligation to Save the Family Farm?*, edited by Gary Comstock, 347–360. Ames, IA: Iowa State University Press, 1987.

Boehlje, M. "Industrialization of Agriculture: What Are the Implications?" *CHOICES* 11 (First quarter, 1996): 30–33.

Bridges, William. *Managing Transitions: Making the Most of Change.* Reading, MA: Addison-Wesley, 1993. 130 pp.

Brown, Lester. *Who Will Feed China? Wake-Up Call for a Small Planet.* Worldwatch Environmental Alert Series, ed. Linda Starke. New York: W. W. Norton, 1995. 163 pp.

Browne, William, Jerry Skees, Louis Swanson, Paul Thompson, and Laurian Unnevehr. *Sacred Cows and Hot Potatoes: Agrarian Myths in Agricultural Policy.* Boulder, CO: Westview Press, 1992. 150 pp.

Bureau of the Census. *Historical Statistics of the United States: Colonial Times to 1970, Bicentennial Edition, Part 1.* Washington, DC: U.S. Department of Commerce, 93rd Congress, 1st Session, 1975.

Buzby, J., and T. Roberts. "ERS Updates U.S. Foodborne Disease Costs for Seven Pathogens." *Food Review* (September–December 1996): 20–25.

Cantrell, Patty, Rhonda Perry, and Paul Sturtz. "The Environment (. . . and Factory Farms)." *In Motion Magazine,* http://www.Inmotionmagazine.com, 1999.

Carlson, G., M. Marra, and B. Hubbell. "Transgenic Technology for Crop Protection: The New 'Super Seeds.'" *CHOICES* 12 (Third quarter, 1997): 31–36.

Castle, E. "The Forgotten Hinterlands." In *The Changing American Countryside: Rural People and Places,* edited by E. Castle, 1–9. Lawrence, KS: University Press of Kansas, 1995. 563 pp.

Center for Defense of Free Enterprise. Web site: http://www.cdfe.org/DOJReport.htm.

Cheeke, P. *Contemporary Issues in Animal Agriculture.* 2d ed. Danville, IL: Interstate Publishers, 1998. 256 pp.

Costanza, R., et al. "The Value of the World's Ecosystem Services and Natural Capital." *NATURE* 387 (1997): 253–260.

Crosson, Pierre. "Will Erosion Threaten Agricultural Productivity?" *Environment* 39 (1997): 4–9.

Crutchfield, S., J. Cooper, and D. Hellerstein. *Benefits of Safer Drinking Water: The Value of Nitrate Reduction.* Agricultural Economics Report No. 752. Washington, DC: U.S. Department of Agriculture, Economic Research Service, 1995.

Crutchfield, S., et al. *An Economic Assessment of Food Safety Regulations: The New Approach to Meat and Poultry Inspection.* Agricultural Economics Report No. 755. Washington, DC: U.S. Department of Agriculture, Food Safety Branch, Economic Research Service, 1997.

Daniels, Tom, and Deborah Bowers. *Holding Our Ground.* Washington DC: Island Press, 1997.

Dobbs, Thomas. "Price Premiums for Organic Crops." *CHOICES* 13 (Second quarter, 1998): 39–41.

Drabenstott, Mark, and Tim Smith. "Finding Rural Success: The New Rural Economic Landscape and Its Implications." In *The Changing American Countryside: Rural People and Places,* edited by E. Castle, 180–196. Lawrence, KS: University Press of Kansas, 1995. 563 pp.

Duram, L. "Organic Agriculture in the United States: Current Status and Future Regulation." *CHOICES* 13 (Second quarter, 1998): 34–38.

Economic Research Service. *Understanding Rural Agriculture.* Agricultural Information Bulletin No. 710. Washington, DC: U.S. Department of Agriculture, Economic Research Service, 1995.

————. *Agricultural Resources and Environmental Indicators, 1996–97.* Agricultural Handbook No. 712. Washington, DC: U.S. Department of Agriculture, Economic Research Service, 1997.

————. Various data and publications from the U.S. Department of Agriculture Web site: www.econ.ag.gov.

Environmental Working Group. Web site: www.ewg.org, 1998.

Erwin, W. "Changing Times: A Farmer's Perspective." *CHOICES* 10 (Fourth quarter, 1995): 36–37.

Fernandez-Cornejo, Jorge, Sharon Jans, and Mark Smith. "Issues in the Economics of Pesticide Use in Agriculture: A Review of the Empirical Evidence." *Review of Agricultural Economics* 20 (1999): 462–488.

Food Marketing Institute. *The Greening of Consumers: A Food Retailer's Guide.* Bellevue, WA: Harman Group, 1997.

————. *Pesticides in the Food Supply.* Media Backgrounder (http://www.fmi.org/media/bg/pests.html), 1998.

Groth, Edward, Charles Benbrook, and Karen Lutz. *Do You Know What You're Eating? An Analysis of U.S. Government Data on Pesticide Residues in Foods.* Washington, DC: Consumers Union of the United States, Public Service Projects Department, Technical Division, 1999. (http://www.consunion.org/food/do_you_know2.htm).

Heimlich, R., et al. *Wetlands and Agriculture: Private Interests and Public Benefits.* Agricultural Economic Report No. 765. Washington, DC: U.S. Department of Agriculture, Economic Research Service, 1998.

Hewitt, T. "Fields for the Future: Latest Farming Research Poses Greener Revolution." *FORUM for Applied Research and Public Policy* 13 (1998): 83–87.

Hipp, Janie. "Right-to-Farm Laws: History and Future." Paper presented at the 1998 National Public Policy Education Conference, Clackamas, OR, September 21–23, 1998. Text available at http://www.farmfoundation.org/1998NPPEC/nppecpapers.htm.

Hoag, D. "Soil Conservation Incentives in the 1985–1996 U.S. Farm-Bills." In *Incentives in Soil Conservation: From Theory to Practice,* edited by David W. Sanders, P. Huszar, S. Smbatpanit, and T. Enters. Enfield, NH: Science Publishers, forthcoming 1999.

Hoag, D., and E. Fathel-Rahman. *The Value of Agricultural Research,* Experiment Station Report. Fort Collins, CO: Colorado State University, forthcoming 1999.

Hoag, D., J. Fulton, and E. Hornbrook. *Colorado's Farm and Food System: Its Contribution to the State's Economy in 1992*. Bulletin 551A. Fort Collins, CO: Colorado State University Cooperative Extension, 1995. 26 pp.

Hocker, J. "Patience, Problem Solving, and Private Initiative: Local Groups Chart a New Course for Land Conservation." In *Land Use in America*, edited by H. L. Diamond and P. F. Noonan, 245–259. Washington, DC: Island Press, 1996.

International Food Information Council. *IFIC Review: Pesticides and Food Safety* (http://ificinfo.health.org/review/ir-pest.htm), 1995.

Jaenicke, E. *The Myths and Realities of Pesticide Reduction: A Reader's Guide to Understanding the Full Economic Impacts*. Policy Studies Report No. 8. Greenbelt, MD: Henry A. Wallace Institute for Alternative Agriculture, 1997.

Jolly, R., and A. Vontalge. *How Many Iowa Commercial Farm Businesses Will Survive Until 2000?* Staff Paper No. 306. Ames, IA: Iowa State University Extension, 1998.

Jones, K. *Landowning Colorado Style*. Business Management, Colorado Association of Soil Conservation Districts, n.d

Kindall, W., and D. Pimentel. "Constraints on the Expansion of the Global Food Supply." *Ambio* 23 (1994): 4–6.

Kinsey, J. "Seven Trends Driving U.S. Food Demands." *CHOICES* 7 (Third quarter, 1992): 26–28.

Kniffen, Dan. "The Alliance Yellow Pages." *BEEF* 32 (Spring 1998): 12–13.

Koontz, S. Personal communication, 1999. Department of Agricultural and Resource Economics, Colorado State University.

Kushner, K. *Environmental Regulation That's Bad for the Economy—and the Environment*. Hudson Briefing Paper No. 134. Indianapolis, IN: Herman Kahn Center, 1991.

Laycock, W. (task force chair). *Grazing on Public Lands*. Ames, IA: Council for Agricultural Science and Technology, 1996.

Lipton, K., and W. Edmondson. "Linking Agriculture to the Economy." *CHOICES* 8 (Fourth quarter, 1993): 22–23.

Loomis, John. *Integrated Public Lands Management: Principles and Applications to National Forests, Parks, Wildlife Refuges, and BLM Lands*. New York: Columbia University Press, 1993. 472 pp.

Loomis, John, and Doug White. "Economic Benefits of Rare and Endangered Species: Summary and Meta-Analysis." *Ecological Economics* 18 (1996): 197–206.

Mackenzie, W., et al. "A Massive Outbreak in Milwaukee of Cryptosporidium Infection Transmitted through the Public Water Supply." *New England Journal of Medicine* 331 (1994): 161–167.

Mills, E. "The Location of Economic Activity in Rural and Nonmetropolitan United States." In *The Changing American Countryside: Rural People and Places,* edited by E. Castle, 103–133. Lawrence, KS: University Press of Kansas, 1995. 563 pp.

Monke, J., M. Boehlje, and G. Pederson. "Farm Returns: They Measure Up to Returns to Other Investments." *CHOICES* 7 (First quarter, 1992): 28–29.

Moore, M., A. Mulville, and M. Weinberg. "Water Allocation in the American West: Endangered Fish versus Irrigated Agriculture." *Natural Resources Journal* 36 (1996): 319–357.

Morrison, R., J. Buzby, and C. Lin. "Irradiating Ground Beef to Enhance Food Safety." *Food Safety* (January–April 1997): 33–37.

National Agricultural Statistics Service. Annual reports for 1982 and 1998. Washington, DC: U.S. Department of Agriculture.

National Commission on Small Farms. *A Time to Act.* Washington, DC: U.S. Department of Agriculture, 1998.

"On the Menu: A Trip to the Doctor." *Newsweek* (September 1, 1997): 30.

Organization for Economic Cooperation and Development. *Agriculture and the Environment: Issues and Policies.* Report of the Secretary-General (51 98 07 1/2P). Paris: Organization for Economic Cooperation and Development, 1998.

Pease, James. *Property Rights, Land Stewardship, and the Takings Issue.* Publication No. EM 8689. Corvallis, OR: Oregon State University Extension Service, 1998.

Powers, T. *Lost Landscapes and Failed Economies: The Search for a Value of Place.* Washington, DC: Island Press, 1996. 304 pp.

Rosenberger, R., R. Walsh, and J. McKean. *Benefits of Ranch Open Space to Local Residents.* Report No. XCM-201. Fort Collins, CO: Colorado State University Cooperative Extension, 1996.

Rozelle, S., J. Huang, and M. Rosegrant. "Why China Will Not Starve the World." *CHOICES* 11 (First quarter, 1996): 18–25.

Smith, Kerry. "Environmental Costing for Agriculture: Will It Be Standard Fare in the Farm Bill of 2000?" *American Journal of Agricultural Economics* 74 (1992): 1076–1088.

Smith, Mark, and Marc Ribaudo. "The New Safe Drinking Water Act: Implications for Agriculture." *CHOICES* 13 (Third quarter, 1998): 26–30.

Sorensen, A., R. Greene, and K. Russ. *Farming on the Edge.* DeKalb, IL: American Farmland Trust, Center for Agriculture in the Environment, Northern Illinois University, 1997.

St. John, Bruce. "ICRP Discussion Points: Family Farms vs. Hog Factories." *In Motion Magazine,* http://www.Inmotionmagazine.com, 1999.

Thompson, N., and L. Haskins. *Searching for "Sound Science": A Critique of Three University Studies on the Economic Impacts of Large-Scale Hog Operations.* Walthill, NE: Center for Rural Affairs, 1998.

Tweeten, L. "Anticipating a Tighter Global Food Supply-Demand Balance in the Twenty-First Century." *CHOICES* 13 (Third quarter, 1998): 8–12.

———. *1995 Farm Bill Brief.* Columbus, OH: Department of Agricultural, Environmental, and Development Economics, Ohio State University, n.d. 3 pp.

Tweeten, L., and L. Forster. "Looking Forward to Choices for the 21st Century." *CHOICES* 8 (Fourth quarter, 1998): 26–31.

University of California at Berkeley. *Wellness Letter* 11 (1995): 2.

U.S. Department of Agriculture. *20th Annual Farm Report to Congress.* Washington, DC: U.S. Department of Agriculture, 1998.

van Ravenswaay, E. *Public Perceptions of Agrichemicals.* Task Force Report No. 123. Ames, IA: Council for Agricultural Science and Technology, 1995.

Vlachos, Evan. Personal communication, 1998. Department of Sociology, Colorado State University, Fort Collins, CO.

Wallace, G. *Public Attitudes about Agriculture in Colorado.* Fort Collins, CO: Colorado State University Cooperative Extension, 1995.

Western Water Policy Review Advisory Commission. *Water in the West: The Challenge for the Next Century.* Final report. Denver, CO: Western Water Policy Review Advisory Commission, 1998. (Downloaded directly from Web site: www.den.doi.gov/wwprac/reports/final.htm).

Wilcove, D., et al. "Quantifying Threats to Imperiled Species in the United States." *BioScience* 48 (1998): 607–615.

World Health Organization/United Nations Environmental Program. *The Public Health Impact of Pesticides Used in Agriculture.* Geneva, Switzerland: World Health Organization/United Nations Environmental Program, 1990.

Chronology 2

Agriculture is the world's oldest profession. In the beginning, people were hunter-gatherers. Humans did not even cook meat until 50,000 years ago. However, we gradually figured out that we could cultivate plants and raise animals to suit our needs, instead of accepting food when and where we found it. The agriculture we know today began around 10,000 years ago, when farmers and livestock producers harnessed nature to grow the kinds of products people wanted, in greater quantities, and at the time people wanted them.[1]

Agriculture in the United States combines two systems that evolved independently in lands separated by an ocean. When Pilgrims brought crops from their homelands, Native Americans were already cultivating corn, sweet potatoes, watermelon, tobacco, and cotton. Native Americans added knowledge as

---

[1] The book *The Living Fields* by Jack Harlan (Cambridge University Press, 1995) is an interesting account of various theories about how agriculture began. He concludes that we cannot find a time or place where agriculture originated and spends his time with a closer look at the combination of events that led us from hunting and gathering to domesticated agriculture. Various theories about why people began to cultivate plants include religion, crowded conditions, population stress, and evolution from gathering.

well as new plant varieties to the European diet. Squanto, a Native American chief, taught Pilgrims to put fish in the soil near corn plants as fertilizer. The merger of these two cultures produced the agricultural success story we know today.

Understanding the events that built agriculture in this country helps put our current crises in perspective. Agriculture has always been hard and it has already been through many changes. I have divided America's development into six agricultural eras: the Settlement and Colonization of the United States, prior to the Declaration of Independence; Early Government and Industry; Growth and Expansion; Business and Government Organization; the Technology Boom; and the Cultivation of Agriculture. A review of these agricultural eras reveals that crises related to change are probably normal for agriculture. It also yields some appreciation for how something that changes as much as agriculture can still be steeped in traditions.

Settlement and Colonization (Prior to 1766)

In 1607, 144 people came from London to the James River in what is now Virginia to establish settlements. Life in the New World was hard. Most of the people who came were adventurers, not farmers. Even the farmers found that what worked in England did not work here. After eight months, only 38 people survived. And by 1622, 4,000 of the 6,000 new arrivals also died. The early settlers had to rely on the bounty of the natural world for hunting and gathering until they gradually learned to tame the new land for agriculture. Ironically, tobacco saved them. The smoking habit swept Europe and provided a staple commodity that supplied much-needed cash to establish agriculture in the New World.

Small land grants were made to individual settlers. But well-connected people gained control over large tracts of land. George Washington, for example, recruited soldiers by offering them land but reneged and gave large parcels to officers instead of providing enlisted men with the small tracts he had promised them. Labor at the time was a great concern to these large landholders. Farmers had large families or they brought in indentured servants or slaves. In the United States, 20 African slaves were first sold in 1619; there were 6,000 African slaves by 1700.

Settlers in the North produced a variety of crops and livestock, primarily for subsistence. Large plantations that grew crops for export were more often found in the South. Farmers near waterways had opportunities for trade. Farming used oxen and horses for power, crude wooden plows, and hand cultivation and harvesting. Most domestic livestock, except turkeys, were imported. Many crops were adopted from Native American varieties, including maize, sweet potatoes, tomatoes, pumpkins, squashes, watermelons, beans, grapes, berries, peanuts, tobacco, and cotton.

Early Government and Industry (1766–1860)

The newly formed government of the United States and its citizens spent the next hundred years basically doing two things: buying or taking land and then giving it back to new Americans. After the Revolutionary War, settlers took British claims against other countries for themselves instead of giving it to the British. Public landholdings were thus expanded through confiscation from British loyalists and Native Americans, by land disposals from large landholders such as the Penns, and from agreements like the Louisiana Purchase in 1803 and the treaty with Spain in 1819 that gave us Florida. Individual American citizens were then given the land through a variety of programs and purchases.

This agricultural era established the land base for our current agricultural system through a variety of land giveaways, discount sales, and indirect incentives such as easy access to railroads. These programs are summarized below. The end of this era characterized the beginning of commercialization in agriculture.

1766   George Washington suggested establishing a National Board of Agriculture. This was the first step toward our continued government involvement in agriculture.

1776   The Declaration of Independence was signed. While agricultural reasons are less often cited, British controls on farm exports, restrictions on land titles, and limitations of western settlement helped push pioneers to declare their independence.

1776   Land grants were offered in exchange for service in the Continental army. George Washington offered land to small peasant farmers in return for serving but reneged and gave the land to officers in the end.

1786   During Shays's Rebellion, armed Massachusetts farmers revolted against agricultural price deflation. Shay was eventually pardoned for leading an attack on the Springfield arsenal and for preventing courts from holding session.

1790   Ninety percent of the United States population was gainfully employed in agriculture (it is currently less than 3 percent).

1793   Eli Whitney invented the cotton gin, which drastically reduced the amount of time it took to clean cotton and prepare it for sale. Whitney's invention was significant because it helped cotton growers, but it was also important because it showed that manual tasks could be automated.

1794   Farmers protested against taxes on grain and whiskey during the Whiskey Rebellion. President George Washington demonstrated federal power to enforce laws by sending in troops.

1796   The Public Land Act of 1796 was instituted. This first large-scale public program to distribute public lands to the masses authorized federal land sales in 640-acre parcels to the public for $2 per acre.

1796   Charles Newbold patented the first cast-iron plow.

1803   Thomas Jefferson authorized the Louisiana Purchase, capitalizing on France's need for cash and purchasing the western drainage area of the Mississippi River. Jefferson did not know the extent of what was purchased, so he sent Meriwether Lewis of Lewis and Clark fame to explore the northern reaches of the region. It contained everything between the Rocky Mountains and the Mississippi River from the Gulf of Mexico to British North America.

1810   The first American agricultural publication, *Agricultural Museum,* was published.

1817   New York City received grain-fed steers during what was probably the first of several historic cattle drives.

1820   The Land Act of 1820 was established. The government sold 80-acre parcels of public land for $1.25 per acre.

1820   The first Agriculture Committee in the U.S. House of Representatives was established. The Senate followed suit in 1825.

1820+   U.S. food-canning industry was established.

1825   The Erie Canal was completed. This amazing engineering feat connected Lake Erie and the Hudson River, making it easier to transport products from the Atlantic to the Great Lakes region.

1830   Marking the beginning of the railroad era, the "Tom Thumb" steam engine ran 13 miles. Railroads played an important part in U.S. development. They brought people to new lands and returned crops to city centers. Railroads are still important to agriculture today, carrying many of our farm and ranch commodities to processors and food products to retailers.

1830   The first soil survey was conducted in Massachusetts. Currently, most of the country's soils are mapped. Soil maps describe the type of soil, what it is capable of producing, and potential environmental concerns like wetlands and salinity. This knowledge plays an important part in targeting crops and inputs and in formulating appropriate policies to protect sensitive soils.

1836   The first public cattle auction was held in Ohio.

1837   John Deere and Leonard Andrus began manufacturing steel plows. By 1857, the plant in Moline, Illinois, was producing 10,000 plows per year. Deere & Company is now one of the leading agricultural equipment manufacturers in the world.

1841   The Preemption Act gave squatters first rights to buy land. People who had been living and producing on unclaimed lands for years were given the right to purchase the land from the government at bargain prices.

1842   The first grain elevator was built in Buffalo, New York.

1845–   The potato famine devastates Ireland. Over a million and
1855   a half people were forced to migrate to the United States
        to avoid starvation and disease. Almost a million people
        who stayed in Ireland died.

1849   During the California gold rush, more than 40,000 people
        were drawn to California in search of gold.

Growth and Expansion (1860–1932)

In the 1850s, one could find commercial agriculture in broad belts
throughout the country. Many farmers and ranchers were still growing crops for subsistence, but some were beginning to grow surpluses for sale off the farm, too. The primary expansion before 1860
came from increasing acreage, not yields. However, during the
growth and expansion period, farmers began producing more food
per acre as well. In addition, market centers began to develop in
Cincinnati, Chicago, Buffalo, St. Louis, and New Orleans. Financial
and structural institutions emerged to buy, store, process, and distribute the commodities shipped from the farms and ranches.

The runaway success of expansionary policies led to a collapse
in farm prices and incomes by the early 1930s. From 1929 to 1933,
farm prices and net farm incomes dropped by half. Despite these
miserable times for farmers and ranchers, this era in general set
the stage for the second great expansion America would see.
America invested in research to succeed land expansion. As
Cochrane (1993, p. 102) puts it, "A science-based agriculture—an
agricultural industry that would grow and develop on the basis of
scientific research and development—was still in its infancy . . .
but all its pieces were in place."

1861   The Homestead Act granted 168 acres to farmers who
        would work the land for five years. Under these grants,
        settlers flooded across the countryside to start farms.
        People could still take advantage of this act into the 1970s.

1861+   Cattle began to run wild and multiply rapidly after the
        Civil War, when many owners went to war and ranches
        were destroyed. By the war's end, cattle prices were one-

tenth as high in Texas as they were in the North. Historic cattle drives began over now-famous routes such as the Chisolm and the Goodnight-Loving Trails.

1862   The Morrill Act established the land-grant system to teach agricultural trades in colleges. Each state was granted 30,000 acres for each senator and representative it had in Congress. Proceeds from sales were invested to create colleges for agriculture and mechanical arts.

1862   The U.S. Department of Agriculture (USDA) was established; it received cabinet status in 1889. The first commissioner of the USDA, Issac Newton, outlined its first objectives:
• Collect, arrange, and publish statistics
• Introduce new plants and animals
• Answer inquiries of farmers
• Test grains, fruits, plants, vegetables, and manures
• Establish a professorship of botany and entomology
• Create an agricultural library and museum

1862–   Farming techniques shifted from using hand power to
1875   horsepower.

1867   The National Grange was organized, originally for social and educational purposes through cooperative efforts. The Grange laws that regulated railroads and grain-storage facilities established the constitutional principle of public regulation of utilities.

1869   Louis McMurray contracted with farmers for vegetables to be canned in his factory, beginning the concept of vertical integration (coordinating two phases of production).

1870   Foot-and-mouth disease was first reported in the United States.

1870   Refrigerator cars were introduced on railroads.

1873   Barbed wire was invented.

1887   The Hatch Act created agricultural research funds for college experiment stations. These funds still drive the research

| 1887 cont. | of land-grant universities today. Experiment stations direct research on campuses and oversee research at outlying research stations. |

1887
cont.   of land-grant universities today. Experiment stations direct research on campuses and oversee research at outlying research stations.

1890   The Morrill Act was broadened to establish separate agricultural colleges for African Americans. There are still 16 "1890" schools in the South today. These schools were basically the land-grant colleges for African Americans. Today, of course, the schools are integrated.

1892   Boll weevils crossed the Rio Grande into the United States. The boll weevil is a small insect that burrows into the cotton boll, wreaking havoc on the cotton industry. In the mid-1980s, boll weevils were eradicated in North Carolina and in parts of many other southern states. Producers spend a great deal of money and risk environmental hazards with their efforts to control boll weevils where they still exist.

1900   The Wright brothers' plane flew at Kittyhawk.

1900–
1910   George Washington Carver pioneered new uses for peanuts, sweet potatoes, and soybeans. Carver showed that crops can be used in many ways as food as well as substitutes for nonfood items, such as soybean ink.

1902   The Farmers' Union was started. Today the Union is largely an advocate of the small and traditionally based farmer.

1902   The first gasoline-powered tractors emerged.

1906   The first county extension agent was appointed. The Cooperative Extension Service in the United States has grown into a model of technology transfer (education) around the world.

1908   President Roosevelt's Country Life Commission was established to address problems of farm wives and to keep children on farms.

1910–
1914   The "Golden Age of American Farming." The Golden Age was used as a reference in the 1970s as the standard against which to index parity because it represented the most "prosperous" time for agriculture.

1911   The first Farm Bureau was formed in Broome County, New York. The Farm Bureau has grown into a powerful advocate of farmers and ranchers today.

1914   The Smith-Lever Act established the Extension Service.

1917   The United States entered World War I. Prices for crops and land rose sharply. Land prices rose 60 percent between 1916 and 1920.

1920+   Postwar farm prices drop sharply. In 1920, corn prices fell from $1.61 per bushel to just $0.49 per bushel from May to December. The price fell to $0.31 per bushel in 1921.

1922   The Capper-Volstead Act legalized agricultural cooperatives. Because of the importance of food, Congress gave agriculture the right to organize in order to gain greater market power in both buying and selling.

1924–   Farm income leveled out, but farmers demanded "equal-
1928   ity for agriculture." President Coolidge vetoed attempts to support farm incomes. Overproduction and low incomes were a harbinger that expansion had ended and that agricultural goals needed to be reconsidered; farm product prices were halved by 1932.

1928   The Future Farmers of America (FFA) was founded. FFA is now a leading organization for agricultural youth.

1929   The National Council of Farmers Cooperatives was organized.

1929   The U.S. stock market crashed in October.

1930   The first federal assistance program for school lunches began. The government continued to subsidize school lunches because it helped youth, farmers, and ranchers.

1931   Due to drought and the depression, 2,294 banks failed. Farmland dried out when economic times were already hard. There was no one to buy farms; prices fell and banks were left holding property worth less than what was owed.

Business and Government Organization (1933–1950)

Farmers and ranchers began this era with a bleak outlook about their future. Expansion on to new lands had worked well, but finding new land suitable for production was becoming difficult. During this period, the government and businesses regrouped and searched for solutions to overproduction and environmental degradation. A variety of new government policies was developed to stimulate and protect agriculture.

1933– Huge dust storms originating from the Great Plains de-
1935   stroyed property and lives. Damages generated public support for the government to promote soil conservation.

1933– Several new programs under the New Deal legislation in-
1940   creased government involvement in agriculture, including soil conservation and grazing controls, programs to stimulate agricultural sales, and the first and most comprehensive commodity price and income support program.

1934   Some parts of the country experienced massive overgrazing. The Taylor Grazing Act controlled unregulated grazing, thus protecting these lands for future generations.

1935   Congress funded the Soil Conservation Service. Now called the Natural Resource Conservation Service, this agency is one of the biggest in the U.S. Department of Agriculture. It is charged with protecting soil resources. Its first chief, Hugh Bennett, was dubbed the "father of soil conservation."

1939   The Food Stamp Program began, a precursor to today's program that helps poor people get food and helps farmers sell more products.

1940– The concept of vertical integration began to take hold
1960   during this 20-year period, especially in the broiler industry. Vertical integration allows better coordination of resources and, many people believe, improves efficiency.

1942   Big commercial beef feedlots emerged. Most beef we con-
        sume today is finished in large feedlots where cattle are
        fed concentrated diets, usually corn. Today more than
        three-fourths of these animals are processed by just four
        packing companies.

1947   General Agreement on Tariffs and Trade (GATT) was
        passed. This groundbreaking agreement opened the door
        for countries to trade more by reducing such barriers to
        trade as embargoes and high import taxes. Eventually, in
        the Uruguay Round of negotiations (1986–1994), world
        leaders agreed that all countries are better off without trade
        protections. Though it will happen slowly, if at all, a series
        of agreements will lead to the dismantling of the world's
        protection of agriculture.

1947   The Federal Insecticide, Fungicide, and Rodenticide Act
        was passed. This program set the human and environmen-
        tal safety standards for pesticides that are released in the
        market.

1949   Along with the Agricultural Adjustment Act of 1938, the
        Agricultural Act of 1949 established the major part of per-
        manent agricultural legislation that is still in effect today.
        These two programs designated mandatory support for
        corn, cotton, and wheat and for certain nonbasic commodi-
        ties (such as wool and honey). This is the default legisla-
        tion if current legislation expires without being replaced;
        it would impose high price supports and an automatic vote
        of producers on whether to implement mandatory pro-
        duction controls.

Technology Boom (1950–1980)

Excess capacity, which led to low prices following World War I,
resurfaced after World War II. A predicted 40 percent fall in prices
was avoided with the advent of government price and income
support programs. Prices dropped in the 1950s but later recovered, and this era began to show the tremendous growth potential
available from new technologies. From 1948 to 1994, growth rates

in productivity increased almost 2 percent every year. These technology gains compounded chronic oversupply problems, so the government experimented with a variety of support programs. However, in the end, farmers, Congress, and others decided to end the programs. The Federal Agriculture Improvement and Reform Act of 1996 phased out most support programs to encourage a market-based approach and greater reliance on capturing international markets.

1950+   Farmers changed from using horses to tractors.

1950   Massive agricultural surpluses began to accumulate.

1954   The Agricultural Trade Development and Assistance Act of 1954 established a U.S. food-assistance program known as PL 480 Food for Peace. This program, still active today, buys from U.S. farmers and donates or provides low-interest food loans for impoverished countries.

1954   The National Wool Act declared wool a strategic and necessary material based on the need for military uniforms, and therefore wool growers got federal price supports. Price supports for wool lost popularity in the 1990s.

1956   The Agricultural Act of 1956 created the Soil Bank, which authorized short- and long-term removal of land from production in return for annual rental payments from the government. This included the Acreage Reserve Program for wheat, corn, rice, cotton, peanuts, and tobacco, and the ten-year Conservation Reserve Program.

1958   The Delaney Clause established the principle that no substance that causes cancer in lab animals, regardless of dose, may be added to food. This clause has created problems in the 1990s as technology makes it possible to measure smaller and smaller traces of chemical residues.

1958   The Humane Slaughter Act helps the concept of animal welfare begin to get a foothold, requiring humane slaughter in packing plants.

1960   More ranchers began using artificial insemination for their herds. Currently, more than 90 percent of dairy cows and 5–10 percent of beef cows are inseminated.

1962   *Silent Spring* by Rachel Carson was published. Many people believe that this book marked the beginning of the environmental movement in agriculture. Carson argued that dichlorodiphenyl trichloroethane (DDT) and other pesticides were bad for the environment and therefore for society.

1964   Ruth Harrison wrote *Animal Machines* in Britain. Her alarm stirred concern, and the Brambell Committee was formed in Britain the following year to investigate the abuses of animal welfare in livestock production.

1964   The Food Stamp Act of 1964 formed the basis for food stamps, which give poor people the means to buy agricultural commodities. Currently, this program spends nearly half of the total U.S. Department of Agriculture budget.

1964   The Chicago Mercantile Exchange began offering live cattle contracts. The futures market provided a valuable way for producers to transfer risk to someone else.

1965   The recommendations of the Brambell Committee in Britain led to an end of debeaking, docking of pig's tails, and tethering of sows and veal calves. The committee declared all livestock must be given the freedom of movement to turn around, groom, get up, sit or lay down, and stretch limbs.

1965   The first multiyear farm legislation, the Food and Agricultural Act of 1965, was passed for wheat, feed grains, and upland cotton. Farmers were paid to not produce in voluntary acreage-control programs. Price and income supports protected earnings, and disposal programs for surplus crops in domestic and foreign markets provided outlets for overproduction.

1970   The Agricultural Act of 1970 established a set-aside program that required farmers to set some land aside in return

1970
cont.

for receiving commodity price and income support payments. It also established payment limits for any single
individual.

1970

Norman Borlaug received the Nobel peace prize for developing high-yielding wheat varieties.

1970

Consumer activism began to intensify about beef prices,
nutrition, and health.

1970

The government created the U.S. Environmental Protection Agency, which now plays a large role in agricultural
production by monitoring and regulating water quality,
air quality, and waste management.

1972

Russians bought great quantities of U.S. wheat, escalating
prices dramatically. This led to the now-infamous statement in 1973 by then–Secretary of Agriculture Earl Butz,
"Plant fence row to fence row," which intensified oversupply problems since export demand did not hold.

1973

The Agriculture and Consumer Protection Act of 1973 established target prices and deficiency payments to replace
price supports.

1973

DDT was banned because of suspected hazards to the environment, especially to bird populations.

1973

A price freeze by President Nixon leads to devastation in
the cattle industry (the price of fed cattle dropped from 80
cents to 38 cents per hundredweight). Grain exports rose.

1976

Farmers wanting parity with the "Golden Age of American Farming" in 1910–1914 create the American Agricultural Movement.

1977

The American National Cattlemen's Association and the
National Livestock Feeder's Association merge to form the
National Cattlemen's Association (changed to the National
Cattlemen's Beef Association in 1996).

1978

The first calf from a frozen embryo was born in the U.S.

1979   The American Agricultural Movement organized a "tractorcade" demonstration in Washington, D.C., which flooded the city with tractors.

The Cultivation of Agriculture (1980–present)

Agriculture has been remarkably productive, so much so that people have questioned whether we have gone too far in the name of increased production. Between 1960 and 1980, several books and articles challenged agricultural practices, setting the stage for the need to "cultivate agriculture." Agriculture has proven it can do many things, but there is little agreement about what it *should* do. Compatibility problems have intensified over how animals should be treated, what is appropriate land use, and when, where, and how much pollution or resource degradation is acceptable in the name of production. In short, agriculture is having trouble fitting into society. Competing and often conflicting policies and events that reflect society's changing preferences, therefore, characterize this era.

1980s   In the early 1980s, several farms failed due primarily to overexpansion during the 1970s. Farmers recovered by the end of the decade.

1980–   The television program *60 Minutes* ran stories on hog ma-
1985   nure in North Carolina and on poultry processing.

1980–   Cover stories appeared in *Time, Newsweek,* and *Reader's*
1985   *Digest* entitled "How Safe Is Your Food?" "Is Anything Safe?" and "The Battle over Animal Rights," respectively.

1981   The Agricultural Act of 1981 boosted farm supports, resulting in higher prices and lower exports. These consequences contributed to large farm failures in the mid-1980s.

1981   Companies build the first pig megafarms. Concentrated animal-feeding hog farms became one of the most controversial issues of the day. Farms can get so big that they generate more waste than many small cities.

Mid-   Farm income crises. Land values crash between 30 and 60
1980s   percent.

1984   The Union Carbide plant explosion killed 3,000 people in
        Bhopal, India. Lower industry standards were blamed for
        the explosion of this plant that manufactured agricultural
        pesticides. Less developed countries accused the United
        States of being arrogant and greedy.

1985   The Food Security Act of 1985 lowered farm price and in-
        come supports, lowered dairy supports, and created sig-
        nificant new conservation provisions. The Conservation
        Reserve Program idled 36 million crop acres, conservation
        compliance required soil conservation to get government
        price and income supports and to receive loans, and the
        Sodbuster program prevented new highly erodible land
        from being converted to farmland. Swampbuster similarly
        prevented wetlands from being converted. The Dairy Ter-
        mination Buy-Out of 1986 affected 14,000 dairy farmers.
        The beef industry lost $25 million.

1986   Farm price and income support program costs hit $26 bil-
        lion due to low prices, overproduction, and poor exports.
        (Program costs decreased to $22 billion in 1987.)

1986   Willie Nelson sang at the first *Farm Aid* concerts to help
        failing farmers. These concerts still occur today.

1987   The pork industry launched its "Pork, the Other White
        Meat" advertising campaign.

1988   *Time* named "Earth" the Man of the Year, validating the
        importance of the environmental movement.

1989   The first genetically engineered calves were produced in
        the United States.

1990s   Modification of the General Agreement on Tariffs and
        Trade (GATT) and the North American Free Trade Agree-
        ment (NAFTA) lowered trade barriers on imports and ex-
        ports.

1990s   Fish consumption advisories were issued by states warning consumers of mercury, PCBs, chlordane, dioxin, and DDT found in seafood.

1990   The Food, Agriculture, Conservation, and Trade Act of 1990 extended the conservation and price support concepts defined in 1985's Food Security Act. This reaffirmed the intent of Congress to reduce financial supports for commodities and to pay more attention to the environment.

1990   Peter Singer coined the term "speciesism" (the belief that humans are more important than other species) in his book *Animal Liberation*, comparing it to sexism and racism.

1990   The Food and Drug Administration (FDA) approved the use of irradiation for poultry.

1991   *Diet for a Small Planet* by Frances Moore Lappé popularized the concept of vegetarianism for environmental, socioeconomic, and animal-welfare reasons.

1992   Jeremy Rifkin published *Beyond Beef* and questioned the wisdom of high-technology agricultural production.

1993   Cryptosporidium, a pathogen found in bovine manure and other sources, infected 400,000 Milwaukee residents.

1994   Wolves were reintroduced to Yellowstone. Area ranchers worried that their livestock would be threatened and that the ranchers wouldn't be allowed to defend against them.

1994   Beef-packing companies IBP, Excel Corporation, ConAgra Red Meat Company, and National Beef Packing Company slaughtered 80 percent of fed cattle.

1994   Grazing changes were proposed for public lands. Recreationists and environmentalists argued that public lands were being leased at below-market rates and that cattle and sheep grazing there caused environmental damages.

1996   Dolly the cloned sheep captured international attention because it was cloned from the nucleus of a single adult

1996   mammary gland cell. The nucleus was substituted for the
cont.   chromosomes normally provided by the sperm and egg at
        fertilization. Embryologists had actually been experiment-
        ing with cloning for years. Dolly's birth followed a pro-
        gression of experiments that began in the 1970s.

1996   The Federal Agriculture Improvement and Reform Act of
        1996 removed the link between income support payments
        and farm prices by providing predetermined production
        flexibility contract payments. Many supports will be
        phased out over seven years (2002 will be the last year).
        The act eliminated acreage compliance set-asides in favor
        of a market orientation. This legislation is sometimes called
        "Freedom to Farm" since producers no longer had to worry
        about compliance with government-set planting rules.

1997   More than 40 animal waste spills killed 670,000 fish in Iowa;
        in Illinois, one spill killed 160,000 fish.

1997   Major recalls of ground beef occurred when *E. coli* was
        detected in Hudson Foods products. There have been sev-
        eral recalls of beef related to deaths and illnesses. The most
        prominent was a 25-million-pound recall of hamburger
        from the Hudson Foods plant in Columbus, Nebraska.
        Many fast-food chains such as Boston Market and Burger
        King were affected.

1997   An outbreak of hepatitis A from Mexican strawberries
        made 230 people sick.

1997   The FDA approved the use of irradiation for beef. Irradia-
        tion can reduce the incidence of foodborne diseases, but
        its use is controversial.

1998   Low prices for crop and livestock commodities created
        income crises. The early 1980s saw a severe crash of farm
        prices and incomes. Prices in 1998 appeared to be very low,
        too. Hogs were selling for 15 cents a pound at sale barns
        around the country. Two studies estimated that net farm
        incomes were down as much as 60–80 percent. However,
        yields since then have been very good, and producers

received more than $18 billion in support from the government. At the time of this printing, the final result is too early to predict.

1998   The Texas Beef Group et al., led by Paul Engler and Cactus Feeders et al., sued Oprah Winfrey and her production companies for disparaging remarks about beef that were made on her television show. Howard Lyman, director of the American Humane Society's "Eating with Conscience" campaign, claimed that mad cow disease could easily be spread to thousands of people through meat from infected cows. Oprah responded on the show, "It has just stopped me cold from eating another burger." The cattle producers lost their lawsuit.

1998   The Department of Health in Great Britain reported that 15 people died from the variant of Creutzfeldt-Jakob disease brought on by mad cow disease.

References and Further Readings

Cochrane, Willard. *The Development of American Agriculture: A Historical Analysis.* 2d ed. Minneapolis, MN: University of Minnesota Press, 1993. 500 pp.

Rogers, Earl, and Susan H. Rogers. *The American Farm Crisis—An Annotated Bibliography.* New York: Garland Publishing, 1989. 149 pp.

Taylor, Robert E., and Tom Field. *Beef Production and Management Decisions.* 3d ed. New York: Prentice-Hall, 1998.

Tuszynski, Carol, ed. *Current Trends and Uncertainties for the Future of U.S. Agriculture.* Unpublished report. Fort Collins, CO: U.S. Department of Agriculture, Veterinary Services, Center for Emerging Issues, Animal Plant Health Inspection Service, 1998.

Tweeten, Luther. *Foundations of Farm Policy.* 2d ed. Lincoln, NE: University of Nebraska Press, 1979. 567 pp.

U.S. Department of Agriculture, Economic Research Service. *A History of American Agriculture: 1776–1990.* http://www.usda.gov/history2/front.htm.

Biographical Sketches

3

ost modern-day crises in agriculture
come from challenges to tradition.
Farmers and ranchers don't just grow
food. Their workplace is their home; it's part
of who they are. Thomas Jefferson laid the
groundwork for this "Agrarian Ideology." His
inspiring words made the case that agriculture and its people are special, a sentiment that
is still held today. His ideas were reinforced
by innovators who built the most productive
agricultural system the world has ever seen.
Scientists like Norman Borlaug created a
"Green Revolution" that doubled, tripled, and
even quadrupled crop yields in countries that
desperately needed more food. George Washington Carver and others found hundreds of
new uses for those expanding harvests, like
making ink from soybeans and plastic from
corn. Eli Whitney and John Deere pioneered
equipment to make it easier to plant, cultivate,
and harvest crops. The government developed
research and outreach programs through the
vision of people like Henry Wallace and Seaman Knapp. People like John Tyson pioneered
vertical integration for livestock, in which one
company coordinates production from start to
finish.

In the 1930s, farmers faced the first of
many speed bumps on the road to high-yield

farming. Hugh Bennett discovered that some farming practices erode soil, which can rob future yields and generate giant dust storms like those that swept through the western United States during the dust bowl. Soil conservation is now the leading environmental concern of farmers. Bennett and other naturalists like Aldo Leopold were friendly to agriculture. However, they opened the door for more demanding analysts. For example, Rachel Carson and Lester Brown intensified criticism about the environmental impacts of agriculture, Cesar Chavez fought for the rights of farm workers, Jeremy Rifkin opposes biotechnology, and Peter Singer wants equality for animals. These later leaders questioned the agrarian ideology and challenged the rights of farmers and ranchers to continue their way of life. Now technology has come so far that factory-like settings sever the link with agriculture's cultural past.

The biographies of just a few of the people who made agricul-ture what it is today and those who now challenge it are provided below.

Hugh Hammond Bennett (1881–1960)

Soil erosion is arguably the top environmental concern of American farmers today, and Hugh Hammond Bennett was the "father of soil conservation." The deeply rooted dedication to soil conservation by most farmers grew in no small part from his efforts in the early 1900s. Bennett was raised on a 1,200-acre farm in North Carolina. Tough terrain there made him keenly aware of the potential impacts of soil erosion if left uncontrolled.

Bennett spent two years studying geology and chemistry at the University of North Carolina until he had to drop out due to a shortage of money. After working in a pharmacy, he returned to college and eventually graduated in 1903. It was purely chance that his first job was as a soil surveyor for the Bureau of Soils, writes Brink (1951). Yet it turned out to be ideal, given his zeal for conservation. His experiences mapping and working with soil issues further fueled his passion to control erosion. Gullies on the land and less visible evidence of what he called sheet erosion convinced him that farmers needed to implement soil-conservation techniques to preserve America's cropping capacity and farming livelihoods.

In 1928, Bennett wrote a USDA circular titled *Soil Erosion: A National Menace*. This theme became the centerpiece of his lifetime, as seen in the publications, research centers, and government programs he created. His experiences gave him the needed facts to persuade Congress to appropriate $160,000 for erosion research in 1930. In charge of the program, he established ten erosion research centers across the country. His legendary communication skills and sometime evangelistic love for conservation were instrumental in passing the Soil Conservation Act of 1935. This was the beginning of the Soil Conservation Service, now called the Natural Resource Conservation Service (NRCS). The NRCS serves as a model program for soil conservation efforts around the globe. Bennett was its first chief.

Bennett wrote many books. His most influential was *Soil Conservation*, written in 1939. In its text he described the principles of soil conservation and laid the groundwork for convincing farmers of the need to control erosion.

Norman Borlaug (1914–)

Norman Borlaug won the Nobel peace prize in 1970 for his role in the Green Revolution. Born in Iowa, he became interested in botany and went to the University of Minnesota. By 1941, he held a B.S., an M.S., and a Ph.D. in forestry and plant pathology. He got his first job outside the United States as the director of a Mexican wheat research program, known by its Spanish acronym CIMMYT. This job fostered his interest in helping poor and developing countries improve their crop yields. He accomplished this goal in Mexico and then moved on to work in India and Pakistan, where his efforts won him a Nobel prize.

Borlaug's professional life is a perfect example of the change crises in agriculture. By many accounts, he saved millions of lives by keeping crop production levels ahead of population growth in developing nations like India. These efforts helped avert mass starvation. Borlaug believed that high-yielding crops slow population growth, arguing that a better-fed, higher-income population reduces its birthrates. By 1968, his work assisted Pakistan's attainment of self-sufficiency in wheat production. In the face of proclamations that India could never feed itself, Borlaug helped that country become self-sufficient in cereal crops by 1974.

Even though he achieved so much during the Green Revolution, Borlaug came under fire in the 1980s. After his success in India, he wanted to help increase crop yields in Africa, where crop output has not always kept pace with population growth. However, environmentalists stalled his efforts over concerns that high-tech farming is not sustainable. These methods rely on inputs like fertilizers and pesticides that are not always available and that cause pollution. Borlaug argues that while their intentions may be good, environmentalists are misguided elitists who do not understand that hunger is more pressing than environmental protection. In addition, he believes, they overstate their concerns. Borlaug asserts that using modern methods to produce crops on fewer acres pollutes less than trying to cultivate more acres without high-tech options.

Borlaug is still living. He has saved millions of lives by enabling developing nations to grow more food. He has seen his efforts to increase yields in Africa thwarted, but the tides are now turning back in his direction as environmental groups become more open to the idea of cautious fertilizer use in Africa.

Lester R. Brown (1934–)

Lester Brown is one of the world's leading voices for global awareness about the environment. Since his roots are in farming, he is also one of the leading voices about agriculture. Brown has an M.S. in Agricultural Economics from the University of Maryland and an M.P.A. from Harvard. He is currently president of the Worldwatch Institute, which he founded in 1974. Worldwatch is the watchdog for emerging global trends in the availability and management of resources. The institute publishes a widely read annual publication series called *State of the World* and a host of other influential books and periodicals. These publications have kept the world informed about declining soil productivity, pollution, and overfishing in the world's waters, among other issues.

Before founding Worldwatch, Brown served as an adviser on foreign agricultural policy to Secretary of Agriculture Orville Freeman during Lyndon Johnson's presidency. In 1966, Freeman appointed Brown administrator of the department's International Agricultural Development Service. Brown left government in 1969 to help James Grant, the former head of UNICEF, establish the Overseas Development Council.

Brown has earned many honors and awards. In 1987, he was awarded the United Nations' Environment Prize. He also won the Nature Gold Medal in 1989 and the 1994 Blue Planet Prize. The *Washington Post* called him one of the world's most influential thinkers. He gets his notoriety from his Worldwatch book series and several other publications. In one of his most controversial books, 1995's *Who Will Feed China? Wake-Up Call for a Small Planet*, he questions whether a growing population can continue to feeds its ever-increasing desires.

Rachel Carson (1907–1964)

Born in Springdale, Pennsylvania, Rachel Carson earned a degree in biology from Pennsylvania College. She majored in zoology during graduate school at Johns Hopkins. She became concerned about the ill effects of DDT (dichlorodiphenyl trichloroethane) and other pesticides on the environment while working for the Fish and Wildlife Service between 1935 and 1952. *Reader's Digest* rejected an article she proposed about these dangers in 1945. However, persistence paid off. A friend wrote her a letter in 1958 saying that many of the birds in her private bird sanctuary had died as a result of pesticides used on the property. The letter made Carson angry, convincing her to write a book called *Silent Spring*. Her book became the most influential ever to criticize the use of pesticides, particularly DDT.

Carson's book has three main principles (Hynes 1989): (1) in nature, nothing exists alone—chemicals that target pests wind up elsewhere, including the food we eat and the water we drink; (2) since World War II, the world is being poisoned along with our insects—DDT, for example, is found in remote places of the globe, such as the polar ice caps, where it was never even sprayed; and (3) the use of technology should be based on a reverence for life. To control nature would be arrogant.

Carson spent many years searching for evidence to help prove her theory about the harmful effects of pesticides on the environment. She wrote a book about Long Island residents that were suing the government over the spraying of DDT on their land. The Long Island residents believed that DDT was poisoning their property.

Rachel Carson inspired many people to look more closely at how pesticides affect the environment. Her efforts won her many admirers and awards, including the Audubon Medal and Cullum Medal. However, she was not without her critics. Norman Borlaug warned about the lives that would be lost without the use of pesticides. And Edwin Diamond, an editor at *Newsweek*, accused Carson of caring more about a cat's death than the 10,000 human deaths that might occur from starvation and malnutrition (Hynes 1989). In his book, *Saving the Planet with Pesticides and Plastics*, Dennis

Avery contends that Carson largely got the facts wrong. Overall, bird populations did not fall, cancer rates did not rise, and DDT saved "hundreds of millions" of people from diseases like malaria and typhus that are carried by insects, contends Avery.

George Washington Carver (1865–1943)

George Washington Carver, born a slave on a Missouri farm during the American Civil War, was freed shortly after birth. His many accomplishments demonstrated for many people how the freedom of African Americans could lead to improved lives and prosperity. Remarkably, he earned a B.S. degree from Iowa Agricultural College (now called Iowa State University) in 1894 and an M.S. degree in 1896. He started his career as a faculty member where he earned his degrees, but in 1896 he moved to Tuskegee, Alabama, where he worked most of his life. Carver developed industrial products from farm crops. His research, called "chemurgy" in his day, resulted in 325 products from peanuts, 108 products from sweet potatoes, and 75 products from pecans.

Carver developed a multitude of products we use today, including axle grease, bleach, cheese, chili sauce, shampoo, wood stains, and ink. In all, he is responsible for 118 industrial products from agricultural commodities and more than 500 dyes and pigments. In 1927, he developed a process for producing paints and stains from soybeans, which earned him three patents.

The world has honored Carver several times, and many of our country's public places bear his name. President Franklin Roosevelt dedicated a national monument to him in 1943. He earned the Spingarn Medal in 1923 and was made a member of the Royal Society of Arts in London in 1928.

Cesar Chavez (1927–1993)

A hero of the American farm laborer, Cesar Chavez raised public awareness and increased protection of farm workers' rights by fighting effectively for a better, safer working environment. His concern came from personal experience. He was born near Yuma, Arizona, in 1927. After losing their farm in the Great Depression, his family looked for a new life in California. However, they did not find a better life. They discovered instead what it was like to be a migrant worker. Chavez moved around so much that he attended more than 30 different schools before dropping out to work full-time in the fields. During the last two years of World War II, he served in the U.S. Navy.

Chavez began his political career in the early 1950s by volunteering for the Community Service Organization (CSO). CSO helped the poor and politically powerless create their own organizations. Chavez worked his way up to became general director in 1958. He resigned in 1962 to cofound the National Farm Workers Association (NFWA) with Dolores Huerta. The NFWA grew steadily. It built on small victories gained throughout California, winning pay increases for workers in the Delano area in 1965, for example. In 1968, he organized migrant grape pickers, which became a major breakthrough for the NFWA. Chavez sought the aid of a variety of groups (including civil rights and religious organizations, major newspapers and magazines, and political leaders such as Robert F. Kennedy) as he leveraged the local issue into the national agenda. The strike continued in one form or another for 30 years.

The NFWA became the most powerful representative organization for farm workers in the United States. It now goes by the new name of the United Farm Workers of America. Among Chavez's other accomplishments are the establishment of a burial insurance program, a union newspaper called *El Malcriado*, a farm workers' credit union, a retirement village, a theater troupe, a pension fund, and a farm workers' service center.

John Deere (1804–1886)

John Deere is the Henry Ford of agriculture. He started as a blacksmith in Vermont, but in 1836 he caught the bug to head west. He sold his business and traveled to Illinois by canal boat, lake boat, and stagecoach. The town of Grand Detour, Illinois, was in bad need of a blacksmith, so he built a forge and started business within two days.

At first he served as an ordinary blacksmith. Within a year, however, he noticed some of the pioneers were leaving the area because the unusually rich soils clung to the plow bottoms, which then had to be scraped every few steps. John Deere turned the tables by shaping a moldboard plow from polished steel he made out of a broken saw blade.

Deere's plows proved to be successful in the stubborn Illinois soils. But what made him truly different is that he made more plows than his local customers demanded, and he traveled around the countryside to sell his farm equipment. Blacksmiths at that time usually did only custom-order jobs. Ten years after he made his first plow, he was making and selling 1,000 per year—he even had to order a roll of steel from England in 1843 to supply his needs. By 1857, his factory in Moline was selling more than 10,000 plows per year.

Deere's solid reputation for manufacturing high-quality agricultural equipment continues today. Deere & Company is now one of the leading agricultural equipment manufacturers in the world. He continued to manage his company until he died in 1886.

Paul Engler (?–)

Paul Engler owns Cactus Feeders, Inc., the largest privately held feeding operation in the world. In 1996, when Engler was honored by the National Cattlemen as the Business Man of the Year, his holdings were worth $650 million. Cactus Feeders, with a onetime capacity of over 330,000 head of cattle, includes five feedyards and operates farms and ranches in Texas, Colorado, New Mexico, and Nebraska. It represents large cattle-feeding operations in the west, which are typical in the cattle industry but the subject of controversy today. The cattle industry is struggling to compete with integrated swine and poultry industries on one hand and cattle producers who want to maintain their traditional production habits on the other.

Engler is personally best known for his civil lawsuit against Oprah Winfrey in early 1998. He argued that she allowed her TV-show guests to present information about the cattle industry that he believed was false, which he claimed cost him and his coplaintiffs more than $10 million. Howard Lyman, director of the American Humane Society's "Eating with Conscience" campaign, said on the show that cows were being fed the carcasses of other cows that had died in the feedlots. Lyman also stated that mad cow disease could easily be spread to thousands of people through meat from infected cows. Finally, he said that mad cow disease could make "AIDS look like the common cold."

Thirteen states have outlawed unsupported allegations against foods. These "veggie libel laws" protect farmers and ranchers from false claims about their products. Nevertheless, Engler and his coplaintiffs lost their case, dealing a blow to the libel laws. Engler is appealing the decision and 130 people who feed cattle in his feedlot are filing a new suit.

Dolores Huerta (1930–)

Dolores Huerta is the cofounder, with Cesar Chavez, and now secretary-treasurer of the United Farm Workers of America (UFW), originally known as the National Farm Workers Association (NFWA). She is recognized for her efforts in the civil rights movement, especially related to agricultural labor. Her accomplishments include negotiating the first collective bargaining agreement for farm workers and helping escalate a local grape-picking labor dispute to a nationwide boycott. She has a long track record of successful lobbying efforts for the UFW. Huerta has been arrested 22 times in displays of civil disobedience, yet she found time to raise 11 children.

Huerta was born in New Mexico. She comes by her activism honestly because her father was a union activist and state assemblyman. She moved to the town of Stockton in the San Joaquin Valley when she was just five years old. Her mother owned and operated a restaurant and hotel, often helping farm workers with food and lodging at no cost.

Huerta received a degree from the University of Pacific's Delta Community College but stayed with her teaching job after graduation for only a few months. Activism was in her blood. Her activist career began when she organized the Stockton chapter of the Community Service Organization (CSO), where she met Cesar Chavez. Together they formed the NFWA in 1962 when the CSO turned down a request by Chavez to organize farm workers.

Huerta was inducted into the Women's Hall of Fame in 1993. Additionally, she helped pass major legislation for farm workers, like the Immigration Act of 1985, and cofounded the Farm Workers Credit Union, the National Farm Workers Center, Inc., and the Juan De La Cruz Worker Pension Fund. UFW reports that she still works long hours promoting farm workers' causes.

Thomas Jefferson (1743–1826)

Thomas Jefferson is most famous for authoring the Declaration of Independence and serving as the third president of the United States. He was born at the Shadwell tobacco plantation, which was owned by his father, in upcountry Virginia. He graduated from William and Mary College in 1762 and then studied law for five years. According to John Adams, Jefferson had already built a reputation for his prowess in literature, science, and composition when he arrived in Philadelphia in 1775. He came as a Virginia delegate to the Second Continental Congress.

Jefferson is listed here because he is probably the most influential and eloquent advocate of agriculture the world has ever seen. His "Agrarian Ideology" still reflects what the majority of people think today. According to Jefferson, "Cultivators of the earth are the most valuable citizens. They are the most vigorous, the most independent, the most virtuous, and they are tied to their country, and wedded to its liberty and interests, by the most lasting bonds" (Koch and Peden 1993, p. 351). Despite the changes occurring in agriculture today, Jefferson seems to have captured the heart of its lasting qualities when he wrote about it more than 200 years ago.

Jefferson was a true visionary. His skillful prose in the Declaration of Independence has had a lasting impact, he sent Lewis and Clark to explore the West, he made the Louisiana Purchase, and he managed to have time to write philosophy on subjects ranging from agriculture to music. As a farmer, public official, legislator, diplomat, and executive, he is the one of the most quoted men in history.

In his final years, Jefferson overspent on libraries and the arts; on his estate, Monticello; on his guests; and on his children's education. These expenses and others strained his finances to the point that he petitioned the Virginia legislature to dispose of Monticello by lottery. His popularity brought $16,000 in donations from admirers. He died in 1826 on the Fourth of July.

Seaman Asahel Knapp (1833–1911)

As the founder of the Cooperative Extension Service (CES), Seaman Knapp's on-farm demonstrations and his ability to organize farmer-education groups were so successful that Congress passed the Smith-Lever Act of 1914 to establish a CES in every state. The CES now serves as a model for passing on technology to end users that has been copied worldwide.

A native of New York, Knapp graduated from Union College in 1859 and moved to Iowa, where he became interested in scientific farming and stock breeding. He devoted his life to combining his love for agriculture with his passion to improve education. He cofounded the Iowa Improved Stock Breeders' Association and served as its first president. In 1872, he published *The Western Stock Journal and Farmer* out of Cedar Rapids, Iowa. He was a friend of Henry Wallace, who published *Wallaces' Farmer*. Together Wallace and Knapp inspired the government's research-and-extension network that we know today.

Knapp gained a reputation as a visionary and pioneer of agriculture. He became a teacher at the Iowa Agricultural College, now called Iowa State University, and rose to become its second president. He was appointed a special agent for the promotion of southern agriculture by the U.S. secretary of agriculture in 1902. In this capacity, he improved methods of farming and introduced new techniques across the Southwest. For example, he brought rice production to the Southwest and taught Texans ways to control the boll weevil in cotton. The U.S. Department of Agriculture now sponsors a memorial lecture series under Knapp's name to commemorate his life and work.

Aldo Leopold (1887–1948)

Aldo Leopold created the concept of wilderness areas, and he has been called "the father of the modern conservation movement." His roots stem from the Iowa farm where he was born, but he served most of his life as a forest ranger and wildlife ecologist. He graduated from the Yale School of Forestry in 1909 and took a job with the National Forest Service as a game-management specialist. His book, *Game Management*, concerning the protection and care of wildlife in parks and forests, has become a classic.

In 1933, he accepted a job at the University of Wisconsin in the Department of Agricultural Economics as the nation's first professor in game management. It was there that he began to think and write about human attitudes toward wild things and conservation. Leopold eventually became an adviser to the United Nations on conservation. He was partially responsible for the creation of the Gila Wilderness Area in 1924, which was the first designated wilderness area in the world.

Leopold is probably best known for another book he wrote, *A Sand County Almanac*, which describes the interrelationship between a person and his surroundings. He based the text on his work experiences and his efforts to restore a worn-out farm he bought for his family in Wisconsin. *A Sand County Almanac* was not published until 1949, a year after Leopold's death. However, the book had a profound impact on the way people think about conservation.

In his words from *A Sand County Almanac* (p. xviii), "We abuse land because we regard it as a commodity belonging to us. When we see land as a community to which we belong, we may begin to use it with love and respect." Leopold was sympathetic to the farmers' need to be economically feasible, but he believed that they should also consider the land ethic—that is, to examine what is ethically and aesthetically right, as well as what is economically expedient.

Barbara McClintock (1902–1992)

Dr. James Watson called his colleague, Barbara McClintock, one of the three most important figures in the field of genetics. Nevertheless, she was a woman 30 years ahead of her times. In 1983, at age 81, McClintock won a Nobel prize in physiology or medicine for discovering the phenomenon of "jumping genes," more than 32 years after publishing her research. Her finding helps molecular biologists identify, locate, and study genes.

McClintock's background was in agriculture, although her discoveries were far more reaching. She earned her Ph.D. in botany from Cornell University in 1927. She worked at Cornell for a while, and then as a professor in the Botany Department at the University of Missouri until 1941. She did not receive much recognition or support in her early years, although some people, like Marcus Rhoades, recognized her genius quickly. Later, her colleagues said that she was just too far ahead of her times and that her work was too complicated to read and understand then.

In 1941, McClintock joined the group of geneticists at Cold Spring Harbor, where she eventually made her discovery of genetic transposition, or jumping genes, while studying maize. It took other researchers 20 years to identify the same concepts while working with far simpler life-forms.

Much later in life, McClintock was bestowed with many awards as tribute to the importance of her work. Among these were honorary degrees from Harvard and Rockefeller University, a lifetime MacArthur Fellowship, the Laureate Award, the Lasker Award for Basic Medical Research, and the Wolf Foundation Award.

Jeremy Rifkin (1945–)

Jeremy Rifkin might be the world's most popular agricultural technophobe. He rejects most advanced technologies, fearing that they may unleash unknown terrors on society. His activism bloomed early in a variety of peace groups, and in 1968 he helped organize a march on the Pentagon in Washington. In the late 1970s, Rifkin began speaking out against biotechnology, which earned him an "anti-science" reputation. Rifkin believes that biotechnology will eventually lead to Nazi-type attempts to genetically create a master race. For example, Rifkin has opposed a synthetic microbe called Frostban that protects plants from frost. He is also afraid that oil-eating bacteria released into oceans to clean up oil spills might become renegades that multiply in the environment with unknown effects.

Rifkin's main focus now is to reduce the consumption of beef by 50 percent by the year 2000. In 1993, he wrote a very popular book called *Beyond Beef: The Rise and Fall of the Cattle Culture,* and he is the head of the Beyond Beef Coalition. He believes that cows contribute to global warming by producing too much methane, although Avery (1995) contends that cows do not produce anywhere near as much methane as oceans, freshwater, or termites do. Rifkin also asserts that beef consumption has led to increased hunger, disease, and environmental devastation.

Rifkin has captured the attention of many people who fear that technology has gone too far. For some, whether he is right or wrong depends on the technology being discussed. Cloning sheep, for example, is probably more controversial than breeding a strawberry gene into a tomato. Rifkin and his supporters oppose most technology, and he continues today to fight against biotechnology and other advances that rely heavily on technology.

Peter Singer (1946–)

The animal rights movement started over a century ago, but Peter Singer made it popular. He is known worldwide for his book *Animal Liberation.* First published in 1975, some people call his book "the Bible of the animal liberation movement" (Finsen and Finsen 1994, p. 298).

Singer was born in Melbourne, Australia, in 1946. He graduated from the University of Melbourne in 1967 and received a Bachelor's degree in philosophy from the University of Oxford in 1971. He taught at the University of Oxford, New York University, the University of Colorado at Boulder, the University of California at Irvine, and La Trobe University. Until recently Singer served as professor of philosophy, codirector of the Institute of Ethics and Public Affairs, and deputy director of the Centre for Human Bioethics at Monash University, Melbourne. In July 1999, he became the Ira W. DeCamp Professor of Bioethics in the University Center for Human Values at Princeton.

Singer contends that we should consider nonhuman rights similarly to human rights. Anything less amounts to speciesism. To consider rights along the lines of species makes no more sense, according to Singer, than defining rights based on race or gender. He takes the view that there is no rational reason why the interests of animals should be given lesser status than those of humans. We should be concerned with any sentient being—one that has the ability to detect pain and pleasure. Perhaps Singer's greatest contribution has been to describe a new way of thinking about animal rights, one in which we consider the interests of animals when deciding how to treat them. He does not say that equal consideration means equal treatment. A pig, for example, would not want or need to vote.

Singer is a very accomplished writer. Besides his seminal book noted above, he wrote *Democracy and Disobedience, Practical Ethics, The Expanding Circle, Marx, Hegel, Animal Factories* (with Jim Mason), *The Reproduction Revolution* (with Deane Wells), *Should the Baby Live?* (with Helga Kuhse), *How Are We to Live?*, and *Rethinking Life and Death.* He has also edited or coedited *Test-Tube Babies, In Defense of Animals, Applied Ethics, Animal Rights and Human Obligations, Embryo Experimentation, A Companion to Ethics, The Great Ape Project: Equality beyond Humanity,* and *Ethics.*

John Tyson (1904–1967)

The Tyson Food Company is the largest poultry organizations in the world. It brings in about $8 billion a year and has 73,000 employees in the United States alone. The company currently uses 7,429 contract growers. It produces 2 billion chickens, 1.6 million hogs, and 9 million turkeys per year.

John Tyson, the founder of the company, began with a single farm hatchery. He was a trucker who had been transporting chickens from the farm to the market for extra money after the fruit season was over. In 1936, he transported 500 chickens from a farm in Arkansas to a Chicago market in his battered old truck because he heard that more money could be made off poultry in the North. He made a profit of $235, which gave him the desire to start a chicken hatchery of his own. He bought a few incubators and began selling baby chicks to growers. He also became a commercial feed dealer.

In 1943, the Tyson organization purchased a 40-acre tract of land, which became its first commercial farm. Tyson began selling poultry products and feed. The business started to expand rapidly. By 1950, the Tyson Company was producing about 96,000 chickens per week. During the late 1950s, the Tyson Company built its first processing plant at a cost of $90,000. The market fluctuated greatly throughout the 1960s, but the Tyson Company stayed in business. It experienced both record highs and record lows. The production costs exceeded the cost of broilers for 34 consecutive weeks in 1961, forcing the company to sell about 100,000 shares of stock at $10.50 a piece. In 1966, John Tyson's son, Don Tyson, was appointed president of the company. One year later, both John Tyson and his wife, Helen, were killed in a car accident.

Tyson is listed here for his innovative contributions to vertical integration, which allows one company to control production from beginning to end. He showed that one company could control a product from the egg to the consumer's table at a lower cost by coordinating production and marketing activities. Of course, Tyson is not without his critics, too. Vertical integration is blamed for everything from the destruction of the family farm to mass destruction of the environment.

Henry Cantwell Wallace (1866–1924)

Henry C. Wallace is part of an amazing legacy of agricultural leaders. His father, also named Henry, was a preacher and a farmer. Uncle Henry, as his father was called, founded and served as first editor of *Wallaces' Farmer*. This publication's widespread and powerful influence in the Midwest helped the Wallaces leave a lasting impression on American agriculture.

Henry C. Wallace also served as an editor of *Wallaces' Farmer*. He started in 1916 when his father died. In 1921, he became the secretary of agriculture under President Warren Harding. Despite corruption in the Harding administration, Wallace earned a reputation for understanding the business of agriculture and its conservation needs as well. He established the Bureau of Agricultural Economics and worked tirelessly to promote farm exports. At Wallace's death, famed forester Gifford Pinchot complimented his conservation efforts in Alaska and his defense of national forests in the United States.

Henry C. died unexpectedly in 1924. His son, Henry Agard Wallace, took the position of Secretary of Agriculture in 1932, and in 1940 became the country's vic-president during Roosevelt's third term in office. Henry A. founded what is now called Pioneer

Hi-Bred International, Inc., which is worth in excess of $2 billion. Henry A. is largely responsible for the idea that the government should support agriculture.

Eli Whitney (1765–1825)

Many people consider Eli Whitney to be one of the first pioneers in the creation of automated machines. Whitney was born in Massachusetts and went to college at Yale. After graduating, he invented a machine called the cotton gin that drastically reduced the amount of time it took to clean cotton and prepare it for sale. The cotton gin separated unwanted materials, such as seeds and hulls, from cotton. Whitney invented the cotton gin to replace slow, labor-intensive methods that could not keep pace with the extreme demand for cotton at the time.

Whitney invented the cotton gin at the request of a plantation manager named Phineas Miller who wanted a faster way to clean cotton. Whitney did not profit from the cotton gin since his 1794 patent wasn't validated until 1807, leaving time for numerous people to imitate his design. Nonetheless, Whitney's leadership in inventing the cotton gin caused a big advance in the cotton industry and stimulated others to follow with other agricultural innovations. Since then, several technological advances in automated machines have made farmers' lives much easier and more efficient.

When Whitney got a contract to produce muskets in 1798, he proved that unskilled workers could produce parts that normally required skilled workers. His firearms factory in New Haven, Connecticut, was one of the first to use such mass-production methods—another Whitney legacy.

References and Further Readings

Hugh Hammond Bennett
Bennett, Hugh Hammond. *Soil Conservation.* New York: McGraw-Hill, 1939.
Brink, Wellington. *Big Hugh: The Father of Soil Conservation.* New York: Macmillan, 1951.
http://www.nhq.nrcs.usda.gov/CCS/history/HHBspchs.html
Norman Borlaug
Bickel, Lennard. *Facing Starvation: Norman Borlaug and the Fight against Hunger.* Pleasantville, NY: Reader's Digest Press, 1974.
Easterbrook, Gregg. "Forgotten Benefactor of Humanity." *Atlantic Monthly* 279 (January 1997): 75–82.

Lester R. Brown
Brown, Lester. *Building a Sustainable Society.* New York: W. W. Norton, 1981.
http://www.worldwatch.org/bios/brown.html

Rachel Carson
Avery, Dennis. *Saving the Planet with Pesticides and Plastic.* Indianapolis, IN: Hudson Institute, 1995.
Carson, Rachel. *Silent Spring.* Boston: Houghton Mifflin, 1962.
Hynes, Patricia. *The Recurring Silent Spring.* New York: Pergamon Press, 1989.
http://ethics/cwru.edu/carson/main.html

George Washington Carver
Neyland, James. *George Washington Carver.* Los Angeles: Holloway House, 1996. 203 pp.
http://www.lib.lsu.edu/lib/chem/display/carver.html

Cesar Chavez
Taylor, Ronald B. *Chavez and the Farm Workers.* Boston: Beacon Press, 1975.
http://www.whitfield.st-louis.mo.us/students/vandervea/port/
chavez.htm

John Deere
Broehl, Wayne G. *John Deere's Company: A History of Deere & Company and Its Times.* New York: Doubleday, 1984.
http://www.virtualvermont.com/history/jdeere.html

Paul Engler
Hayenga, M. "Texas Cattle Feeders v. Oprah Winfrey: The First Major Test of the 'Veggie Libel Law.'" *CHOICES* 13 (Second quarter, 1998): 13–20.
http://www.wizvax.net/cactus/index.html

Dolores Huerta
Huerta, Dolores, and Frank Perez. *Dolores Huerta (Contemporary Hispanic Americans).* Orlando, FL: Raintree/Steck-Vaughn, 1996.
http://www.ufw.org/ufw/dh.htm

Thomas Jefferson
Koch, Adrienne, and William Peden, eds. *The Life and Selected Writings of Thomas Jefferson.* New York: Random House, 1993.
http://www.monticello.org/Matters/interests/agriculture.html

Seaman Asahel Knapp
Martin, Oscar Baker. *The Demonstration Work: Dr. Seaman A. Knapp's Contribution to Civilization.* San Antonio, TX: Naylor Co., 1941.
http://www.occe.ou.edu/halloffame/knapp.html

Aldo Leopold
Leopold, Aldo. *A Sand County Almanac.* Oxford, UK: Oxford University Press, 1949.

Meine, C. *Aldo Leopold: His Life and Work*. Madison, WI: University of Wisconsin Press, 1988.
http://www.ag.iastate.edu/centers/leopold/aldoonag.html

Barbara McClintock
Hope Fine, Edith. *Barbara McClintock: Nobel Prize Geneticist (People to Know)*. Berkeley Heights, NJ: Enslow Publishers, 1998.
Kittredge, Mary, Matina S. Horner, and Charlotte Kent. *Barbara McClintock (American Women of Achievement)*. Broomall, PA: Chelsea House, 1991.
http://www.almaz.com/nobel/
http://www.mbl.edu/html/WOMEN/mcclintock.html

Jeremy Rifkin
Avery, Dennis. *Saving the Planet with Pesticides and Plastic*. Indianapolis, IN: Hudson Institute, 1995. 432 pp.
Rifkin, Jeremy. *Beyond Beef: The Rise and Fall of the Cattle Culture*. New York: Plume, 1993. 353 pp.
http://www.nationalcenter.org/dos7126.htm

Peter Singer
Finsen, L., and S. Finsen. *The Animal Rights Movement in America: From Compassion to Respect*. New York: Twayne Publishers, 1994.
Singer, Peter. *Animal Liberation*. New York: Avon Books, 1991. 320 pp.

John Tyson
http://www.tyson.com/corporate/History/default.asp

Henry Cantwell Wallace
Midwest Farming as Portrayed by a Selection from Ding's Cartoons. Des Moines, IA: Pioneer Hi-Bred Corn Co., 1960.
Murray, W., and R. Beneke. "Henry A. Wallace as an Agricultural Economist." *CHOICES* 7 (1992): 22–25.
http://www.gi.grolier.com/presidents/ea/vp/vpwall.html
http://www.hawiaa.org/Wallace/HAWhome.html

Eli Whitney
Green, Constance McLaughlin. *Eli Whitney and the Birth of American Technology*. Boston: Little, Brown, 1956.
http://www.gms.ocps.k12.fl.us/biopage/t-z/whitney.html

Facts, Figures, and Case Studies

4

The purpose of this chapter is to provide supplemental information, such as facts figures, and examples, for the seven crises discussed in Chapter 1: (1) Farm and Ranch Survivability, (2) Modernization, (3) Feeding a Growing World, (4) Safe Food and Drinking Water, (5) Stewardship and the Environment, (6) Urbanization and Land Use, and (7) Country and Urban Conflicts. There is also a section at the end on Government and Society. Each graph, chart, table, or example is ordered by exhibit from 1 to 56. A discussion proceeds each exhibit, as necessary.

It would, of course, be impossible to show all sides of any one crisis. Therefore, a varied sampling is provided to demonstrate the depth and comprehensiveness of each topic. More information can be found in the print and nonprint resources identified in Chapters 6 and 7, giving you ample opportunity to build a greater understanding about any of these areas.

Crisis 1: Farm and Ranch Survivability

Exhibit 1. Output, Input, and Productivity Growth, 1948–1994

The value of input levels used in agriculture have actually gone down by 3–5 percent over the last 50 years. Output levels are about two-and-a-half times higher. Therefore, agriculture today is about two-and-a-half times more productive with the same inputs as it was over 50 years ago.

Source: Ahearn et al. 1998

Exhibit 2. U.S. Agricultural Fact Sheets

Summary sheets about agriculture, like the ones below, are very comprehensive. The same information is available for any state at http://www.econ.ag.gov/epubs/other/usfact/. Information is taken from: the Local Area Unemployment Statistics, county data, Bureau of Labor Statistics; Regional Economic Information System, Bureau of Economic Analysis, U.S. Department of Commerce; the Census of Population, Bureau of the Census, U.S. Department of Commerce; Economic Indicators of the Farm Sector, State Financial Summary, Economic Research Service, USDA; and Foreign Agricultural Trade of the United States, Economic Research Service, USDA.

	POPULATION		
	Total	Metro	Nonmetro
1980 (million)	226.5	176.0	49.6
1990 (million)	248.7	197.8	50.9
Latest (1998) (million)	270.3	215.8	54.5
Per Capita Income (1996 dollars)			
1995	23,918	25,405	18,096
1996	24,436	25,944	18,527
Change	2.20%	2.10%	2.40%
Earnings per Job (1996 dollars)			
1995	29,566	31,316	21,656
1996	29,861	31,580	22,031
Change	1.00%	0.80%	1.70%
Poverty Rate (percent)			
1980	12.4	11.4	15.8
1990	13.8	12.1	17.1
Latest (1997)	13.3	12.6	15.9
Total Number of Jobs (millions)			
1995	149.4	122.3	27.1
1996	152.3	124.9	27.4
Percent of 1995 Employment in Farm and Farm-Related Jobs			
Total	15.2	13.5	23.4
Production	2.4	1.2	7.8
Farm inputs	0.3	0.2	0.8
Processing & marketing	2.2	1.7	4.4
Wholesale & retail	10.0	10.0	10.1

Exhibit 2 (continued)

	FARM CHARACTERISTICS
	1997
Total Land Area (million acres)	2,262.40
Total Farmland (million acres)	945.5
Percent of total land area	41.20%
Cropland (million acres)	431.1
Percent of total farmland	46.30%
Percent irrigated	11.60%
Percent in pasture	15.00%
Percent in Conservation Reserve	5.20%
Woodland (million acres)	71.5
Percent of total farmland	7.70%
Percent in pasture	41.6%
Pastureland (million acres)	396.9
Percent of total farmland	42.60%
Other Land (million acres)	32.3
Percent of total farmland	3.5%
Average Farm Size (acres)	491.0
Farms by Size (percent)	
1 to 99 acres	45.00%
100 to 499 acres	36.70%
500 to 999 acres	9.20%
1,000 to 1,999 acres	5.30%
2,000 or more acres	3.90%
Farms by Sales (percent)	
Less than $50,000	73.60%
$50,000 to $99,999	8.30%
$100,000 to $499,999	14.50%
More than $500,000	3.60%

Exhibit 2 (continued)

	TENURE OF FARMERS
	1997
Full owner (number of farms)	1,146,891
Percent of total	60.00%
Part owner (number of farms)	573,839
Percent of total	30.00%
Tenant (number of farms)	191,129
Percent of total	10.00%
Farm Organization	
Individuals/family corporations (number of farms)	1,719,527
Percent of total	89.90%
Partnerships (number of farms)	169,462
Percent of total	9.00%
Nonfamily corporations (number of farms)	7,899
Percent of total	0.40%
Others (number of farms)	14,971
Percent of total	0.80%
Average operator age (years)	54
Farming as their principal occupation	50.30%

Exhibit 2 (continued)

	FARM FINANCIAL INDICATORS	
	1995	1997
Farm Income and Expense Sheet		
Number of farms	2,071,520	2,057,910
	Million $	Million $
Final crop output	96,655.40	112,497.99
+ Final animal output	87,617.20	96,199.51
+ Services and forestry	19,374.70	22,073.71
= Final agricultural sector output	203,647.40	230,771.21
- Intermediate consumption outlays	109,011.10	118,551.78
+ Net government transactions	.75	.56
= Gross value added	94,710.70	112,275.50
- Capital consumption	18,914.30	19,520.22
= NET VALUE ADDED	75,796.40	92,755.28
- Factor payments	39,057.10	42,931.28
NET FARM INCOME	36,739.30	49,824.00
Farm Balance Sheet		
FARM ASSETS	985,363.70	1,088,841.55
Real estate	761,304.10	849,240.92
Non-real estate	224,059.60	239,600.63
FARM DEBT	151,042.00	165,413.50
Real estate	79,559.80	85,359.39
Non-real estate	71,482.20	80,054.11
EQUITY	834,321.60	923,428.06
RATIOS	Percent	Percent
Debt/equity	18.1	17.9
Debt/assets	15.3	15.2

Exhibit 2 (continued)

	TOP PRODUCTION
Top Five Agriculture Commodities, 1997	% of U.S. Total Value
1. Cattle and calves	17.3
2. Dairy products	10.1
3. Corn	9.8
4. Soybeans	8.8
5. Broilers	6.8

Top Five Agriculture Exports (Estimates), 1997	Million $
1. Soybeans and products	9,253.6
2. Feed grains and products	8,447.6
3. Other	7,350.9
4. Live animals and meat exc. poultry	4,893.4
5. Wheat and products	4,331.1
Total Exports	57,365.1

Top Five Counties in Agricultural Sales, 1997	Percent of U.S.	Million $
1. Fresno, CA	1.40%	2,772.80
2. Kern, CA	1.00%	1,968.50
3. Tulare, CA	1.00%	1,921.40
4. Monterey, CA	0.90%	1,749.70
5. Weld, CO	0.70%	1,286.60
U.S. Total		196,864.60

Source: USDA (http://www.econ.ag.gov/epubs/other/usfact/)

Exhibit 3. Farm Household Characteristics by Sales Class in the Late 1990s

The table on the following page shows the financial status of different farm sizes. Non-commercial farms that sell under $250,000 per year account for 85 percent of all farms but sell only 20 percent of the product. Three-quarters of farms lose over $3,000 per year. However, these small producers manage to maintain a net worth of nearly a quarter million dollars. Just 2.6 percent of farms sell nearly half of the product value each year. Off-farm income is about the same for all farm sizes, but accounts for 108 percent of farm income on small farms and just 16 percent on large farms. Over half of all farms are not in financial trouble.

Notes to Exhibit 3

NA not available
a) 1997
b) 1995
c) Government payments are included in off-farm income
d) Favorable (debt/asset equal or under 0.4 and positive net farm income); Marginal income (debt/asset equal or under 0.4 and negative net farm income); Marginal solvency (debt/asset over 0.4 and positive net farm income); Vulnerable (debt/asset over 0.4 and negative net farm income)

Exhibit 3 (continued)

Item	Noncommercial Farms with Gross Farm Sales of		Commercial Farms with Gross Farm Sales of			
	less than 50,000	50,000–99,999	100,000–249,999	250,000–499,000	500,000 or more	all farms
Number of farm households[a]	1,527,506	187,831	207,058	82,984	53,531	2,058,910
Percentage of farm households[a]	74.2	9.1	10.1	4.0	2.6	100
Percentage of gross cash income[a]	11	9.1	19.1	15.9	44.9	100
Net farm income per farm[b]	(3,384)	4,037	17,801	43,023	164,493	4,706
Off-farm income per farm[b]	43,198	29,330	29,292	29,284	31,332	39,686
Total household income per farm[b]	39,814	33,367	47,093	72,307	195,825	44,392
Share from off-farm sources[b]	108.5	87.9	62.2	40.5	16.0	89.4
Government payments[b,c]	4,453	6,484	11,174	20,048	31,322	6,558
Net worth (equity) per farm[b]	244,861	424,817	514,999	854,804	2,053,665	352,916
Ownership (%)[b]						
Sole proprietor	93.7	90.3	83.6	68.5	52.1	—
Partnership	4.4	5.1	10.8	18.5	22.2	—
Family corporation	1.3	4.3	5.1	12.5	20.3	—
Nonfamily corporation	NA	NA	NA	NA	0.7	—
Farm financial position (%)[b,d]						
Favorable	52.5	57.8	59.6	63.5	58.5	54.3
Marginal income	39.1	25.7	19.2	16.4	13.7	34.4
Marginal solvency	2.6	8.7	13.6	12.8	18.5	5.1
Vulnerable	5.7	7.7	7.6	7.3	9.3	6.2

Source: Constructed from various USDA sources

Exhibit 4. Agricultural Trivia

➤ The U.S. population of farmers and ranchers dropped from a high of 32 million in 1920 to 6 million in 1980 and is estimated to become just 2 million in the year 2000. In the mid-1990s, the total number of people working in farm or farm-related positions was approximately 41 million. The farm population is "graying." There are 20 farmers over 55 for every 1 farmer under 35. The average age of the U.S. farmer is 54.

➤ Total farm and ranchland in the United States reached a high of 56% of all U.S. land in 1940. Since then it has steadily decreased to 43% (year 2000 estimate). Texas led the nation in conversion of farmland to urban land during the period from 1982 to 1992, with 489,000 acres of converted farmland out of 1,402,000 total acres of developed land.

➤ The number of people who are fed by a single farm or ranch has increased from just 22 in 1940 to an estimated 139 in the year 2000.

➤ Every dollar (or every job) produced by agricultural industries generates another one-half to one full dollar (or job) elsewhere in the economy.

➤ It takes only 40 days for an average American to earn enough money to pay for their food supply for an entire year.

➤ In the late 1990s, 2.4% of all farms had sales of more than $500,000, while 74.2% of all farms had sales of less than $50,000. In 1995, over 98% of farms were family operations.

➤ In 1995, commercial farms generated 30 times more sales revenue than noncommercial farms. They accounted for 26% of farms, but 91% of sales. Farms with operators who identified farming as their principal occupation had 4 times more acres and 8 times more income than farms where farming was not the principal occupation of the operator.

➤ In 1995, 91.6% of all farms were sole proprietorships, 5% were partnerships, and 3.4% were corporations. Of the corporations, 3% were owned or closely held by family members.

➤ One-third of U.S. farms received income from government payments in 1995. Commercial farms participated at twice the rate as noncommercial farms.

➤ In 1995, noncommercial farms with gross farm sales of less than $50,000 had an average negative farm income (-$3,384). The average total household income for these farms was positive only because 108.5% of their income was from off-farm sources. Of these farms, 93.7% were owned as sole proprietorships. The majority of the average farm family's income comes from employment off the farm.

Exhibit 4 (continued)

➤ In 1995, about 12.7% of farms sold their products under contracts.

➤ Agricultural exports contributed a total of almost $30 million to the U.S. economy in 1992 through both direct and indirect income. This was over $10 million higher than the next highest exported factor of processing.

➤ In 1997, U.S. consumers spent about 11% of their income on farm products. Of every dollar consumers spent, the U.S. farmer received only 23¢. Labor received 38¢, production received 20¢, packaging got 8.5¢, and interest and taxes received 10.5¢.

➤ Per capita consumption of major domestic animal meats has dramatically increased since the depression era. However, in the 1990s, the overall per capita consumption of chicken has increased at a much higher rate than red meats. From 1980 to 2000 (estimated) alone, annual per capita chicken consumption went from 48 pounds to 80 pounds, an increase of 67%. Beef consumption dropped during this time from 105 to 97 pounds. Pork consumption fared slightly better than beef, as it dropped only 6 pounds per capita, from 73 to 67 pounds during this same time period. Beef consumption reached a high of 161 pounds per capita in 1960. This was 160% greater than pork consumption, and 373% greater than chicken consumption in that same year.

➤ Cattle in feedlots require less than 7 pounds of feed per pound of live weight gain. This is a 10% increase in efficiency over the past 25 years.

➤ Hog farming's contribution to the economy includes a short-run creation of 7–25 jobs, paying $14,000/year for every 1,000 sows, and long-run creation of 14–16 jobs for every 1,000 sows.

➤ National use of conservation tillage in 1996 amounted to 36% of all U.S. farm acres; 26% of farm acres used reduced tillage techniques.

➤ In 1997, 72% of all surveyed waterways were affected by agricultural pollution. In 1990, the EPA found that about 3.6% of wells showed nitrate detections above the 10 ppm level set to protect human health.

➤ In 1997, the Food Marketing Institute found that a total of 52% of consumers in the United States buy with some environmental concern in mind. Of these, 7% were rated as "True Naturals" who express their concern about the environment with virtually all consumption decisions.

➤ President Harry Truman once said, "No man should be allowed to be President who does not understand hogs."

Exhibit 5. Farms, Sales, and Acres Operated by Farm Size, 1997

As shown in Exhibit 3, most farms sell under $250,000 each year and account for few of the sales. This exhibit shows that acres are distributed more evenly.

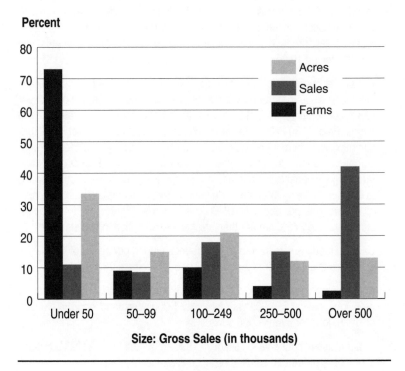

Source: USDA

Exhibit 6. Sources of Income for Average Farm Operator Household, 1996

This figure varies slightly from the table in Exhibit 3 because the data are taken from a different year and source. However, the message is the same. Farm income is a small percentage of a typical farmer's income. The largest income source for most farmers is wages and salaries from off-farm jobs.

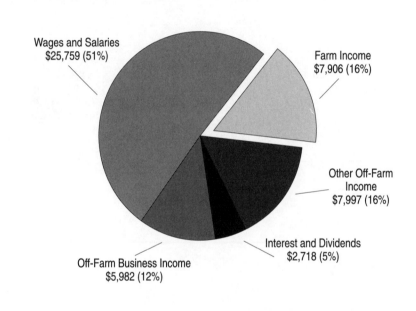

Wages and Salaries
$25,759 (51%)

Farm Income
$7,906 (16%)

Other Off-Farm
Income
$7,997 (16%)

Interest and Dividends
$2,718 (5%)

Off-Farm Business Income
$5,982 (12%)

Source: USDA, Economic Research Service, 1996

Exhibit 7. Legal Organization of U.S. Farms and Ranches, 1995

Individuals or partners operate nearly all the farms and ranches in the United States, despite a common perception that corporations are taking over. Corporations control just 3.4 percent of farms, and only 0.4 percent are not operated by a family. However, corporations and large farms account for a large share of production value.

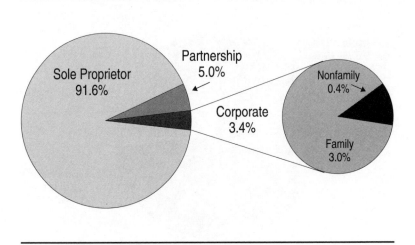

Source: USDA

Exhibit 8. Contribution of Agricultural Sectors to U.S. Income and Employment in 1992 (%)

Farming contributes just 1 percent of the total U.S. income and 1.6 percent of all employment. These numbers jump to the often quoted 15 and 18 percent, respectively, when all phases of agriculture are considered, including wait staff and grocery store clerks. Very few people would likely agree that your local grocery checker is a part of agriculture just because he or she rings up food purchases.

Economic Sector	Income	Employment
Food and fiber	15.7	18.0
Food service	1.5	4.1
Wholesaling and retail	4.1	5.6
Transportation	0.5	0.6
Manufacturing	2.6	2.3
Total inputs	5.9	3.8
Farming	1.1	1.6
Rest of the economy	84.3	82.0

Source: Lipton and Edmondson 1993

Crisis 2: Modernization

Exhibit 9. The Old Agriculture and the New Agriculture

Boehlje describes how modernization has changed agriculture in clear, simple terms. The major theme of the change from the "old" agriculture to the "new" agriculture is the movement away from a family business steeped in agricultural tradition to a business like any other. Commodities are differentiated and targeted to specialty and niche markets, rather than taken down to the local elevator. Operators are increasingly shifting away from owning all of their assets toward renting or leasing them. Markets are shifting away from the United States toward foreign shores. Consumers have enough food and have turned their attention to improved quality, value added and preprocessing, and environmental stewardship. And the public wants a say in how producers grow food and fiber. It is this disjoining of the business of agriculture from the family that has many concerned about industrialization.

Old Concept	New Concept
Commodities	Specific attribute/differentiated raw materials
Staple products	Fashion/niche products/projects
Assets drive the business	Customer drives the business
Hard assets (land, machinery, buildings) are the prime source of strategic competitive advantage	Soft assets (people, organization, plans) are the prime source of strategic competitive advantage
Blending of commodity product from multiple sources	Separation of identity-preserved raw materials
Geographically concentrated production sites	Geographically dispersed/separated production sites
Owning assets	Control of assets
Money/finance/assets are the prime source of power and control	Information is the prime source of power and control

Exhibit 9 (continued)

Labor is a cost and equipment an investment	Labor is an investment and equipment a cost
Sell product and give away service	Sell service and give away product
Expanding and getting into the business (entry)	Contracting and getting out of the business (exiting)
Impersonal/open markets	Personal/negotiated/closed markets
Adversarial relationship with suppliers and purchasers	Partner with suppliers and purchasers
Impersonal sourcing and selling	Relationship sourcing and selling
Insourcing (produce your own) inputs	Outsourcing (buy from someone else) inputs
Outsourcing (buying) from multiple sources	Qualified firm sourcing/sole suppliers
Price premiums for specific attributes and volume purchases	Cost reductions for specific attributes and guaranteed markets
Market (price) risk	Relationship risk
Independence	Interdependence/systems
Stability	Change/chaos/flexibility
Agriculture is an art form	Agriculture is primarily science based
Technical skills critical to success	Human/personal/communication skills critical to success
Technological change and innovation	Institutional (ways of doing business) change and innovation
Core competencies	New/different/unique skills and capabilities

Exhibit 9 (continued)

Tradition/remembering	New ideas/forgetting
Public/open information and research and development	Private/proprietary/closed information and research and development
Resource users and exploiters	Resource protectors
Produce goods and dispose of bads/by-products	Produce goods and bads; utilize/recycle bads/by-products
Agriculture is farming	Agriculture is the food production and distribution system
Family farming and a small business	Industrialized/corporate agriculture
Unstable supply (primarily domestic)	More stable supply (worldwide production)
U.S. is prime world supplier (only store in town)	Many suppliers worldwide
Domestic markets are prime markets	Foreign and industrial markets are critical markets
Raising commodities	Manufacturing food products
Consumers fear high food costs and food shortages	Food costs are a decreasing part of the consumer's budget, and worldwide sourcing reduces the prospects of shortage
Consumers believe their food is safe	Consumers question the safety of their food
Significant political influence	Limited political influence
Adequate budget funds for agriculture	Budget deficits and reduced funding for agriculture

Exhibit 9 (continued)

Farmers are economically disadvantaged	Farmers have comparable income to others
Farm income measures economic well-being	Farm household income measures economic well-being
Operating farmers own most of the farmland	41% of the farmland owned by nonoperators
The public trusts/believes in farmers as stewards of resources	The public questions farmers as stewards of resources
Conservation of resources to maintain/increase productivity	Environmentally sound use of resources to reduce pollution
Efficiency	Ecology
Private property rights are sacred	Society is reserving more property rights for the public and reducing private property rights
Farming is a healthy/safe lifestyle	Farming is a hazardous occupation
Farmers have higher moral standards, a strong work ethic, and generally higher values	Farmers are no different in terms of values, work ethic, or moral standards than the rest of society
Economic well-being of rural communities depends upon farming	Economic well-being of rural communities depends more on nonfarm activity
Rural areas have a higher quality of life compared to urban areas	Rural areas have a lower or at best the same quality of life as urban areas

Source: Boehlje 1995

Exhibit 10. Where the Food Dollar Goes, 1997

Modernization has made activities outside the farm gate more valuable than production on the farm itself. Producers get less than a quarter of every dollar spent on agricultural goods in this country. The rest goes to value-added industries. For this reason, retail consumers often do not feel a large rise or drop in prices at the farm gate when they make purchases at the local grocer.

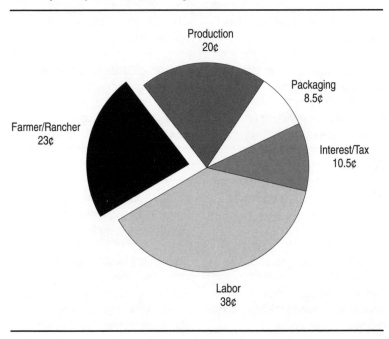

Production
20¢

Packaging
8.5¢

Farmer/Rancher
23¢

Interest/Tax
10.5¢

Labor
38¢

Source: USDA

Exhibit 11. Contracting Arrangements on Farms and Ranches, 1995

Many people worry about contracting since it could diminish market discovery (the process of determining a market equilibrium price). A little over 10 percent of farms use contracts; the rest sell everything in the cash market. Marketing contracts are far more prevalent than production contracts. Contracting, however, heavily controls some markets. These include chicken broilers, fluid milk, cotton, processed vegetables, and citrus.

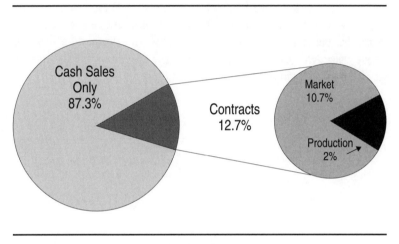

Source: USDA

Exhibit 12. Impact of Various-Sized Hog Operations on Employment, Income, and Government Revenues*

The table on the following page shows that swine farms create about an equal number of off-farm jobs for every job on the farm, regardless of size. In addition, these producers pump income into the community and produce a net government benefit to cities, counties, and schools, as well as generate tax dollars. However, this information shows that several small farms can do a better job in these areas than could one big farm. The benefits shown are for approximately 3,400 animals, which can be produced on one big farm, three medium-sized 1,200-sow farms, eleven 300-head farms, or twenty-three 150-sow farms. The author's of this study found that large farms made a higher income than smaller farms because they produced hogs for a cheaper price. Therefore, despite higher local community benefits from many small farms, private incentives may still favor a big farm.

Exhibit 12 (continued)

	150 sows	300 sows	1,200 sows	3,400 sows
Primary Employment (jobs)	32	34	28	21
Employee Income	925,025	984,230	825,121	709,097
Earnings per Worker	28,907	28,948	29,469	33,767
Secondary Employment	30	31	25	19
Employment Income	490,275	521,642	437,312	375,821
Earnings per Worker	16,343	16,827	17,492	19,780
Total Employment	61	64	53	40
Employee Income	1,415,300	1,505,872	1,262,433	1,084,918
Earnings per Worker	23,202	23,529	23,819	27,123
County Revenues	33,460	38,816	36,490	30,522
County Expenditures	22,655	23,820	19,667	14,414
City Revenues	44,583	47,098	38,895	32,028
City Expenditures	30,509	31,550	26,043	18,592
All Revenue to Local Schools	69,507	76,072	67,259	50,353
Total Local Revenue	147,572	161,997	142,643	112,902
Total Local Expenditures	122,694	131,430	112,969	83,358
Net Benefit	24,879	30,555	29,674	29,544
Net Revenues to State Gov't after Transfers to Local Gov't	54,503	58,274	49,034	43,720
Estimated Local Property Taxes Paid by Operators	30,123	31,708	35,045	27,972

*(Assumes twenty-three 150-sow farms, eleven 300-sow farms, three 1,200-sow farms, and one 3,400-sow farm)

Source: Thompson and Haskins 1998

Exhibit 13. Large-Scale Confinement Hog Farms and Their Potential Impacts on Communities

The impact of large-scale confinement farms is one of the most controversial topics in agriculture today. This exhibit shows that there are pros and cons to these megasized farms. For example, larger farms pay higher wages but use less labor than independent farms. In addition, land prices can go up or down when megafarms move in, depending on whether development or environmental impacts dominate.

Economic Impact	Related Research
Productivity	Recent gains in technology (genetics, pharmaceuticals, and transportation) have concentrated production. Over half of hogs are produced on farms with more than 2,000 animals. Pork production per breeding animal has nearly doubled since 1965.
Employment (Quantity)	In the short run, 7–25 jobs are created, paying $14,000/ year for every 1,000 sows. In the long run, there are 14–16 jobs created for every 1,000 sows. Every job in the swine industry creates 0.25–1.25 jobs elsewhere in the community.
Employment (Quality)	Larger farms pay higher wages (primarily to managers). Larger farms provide better benefits (16% of producers provide 66% of life insurance paid to workers). High turnover on large farms, 17–30%, indicates jobs might not be highly desirable. Many jobs employ people from outside the community.
Health	30–70% of hog industry workers complain of upper respiratory distress.
Taxes	Hog farms pay taxes of up to $17,000 in Virginia and $8,800 in Iowa for every 1,000 sows. There is an estimated $4,000 in tax revenue for every two jobs created.

Exhibit 13 (continued)

Community Services	One new student is enrolled in school for every two new jobs created. More dust, traffic, and accidents are observed. One Iowa community spent $20,000 on gravel for traffic related to a 45,000-head finishing operation.
Real Estate	Real estate prices have gone up in some places from development pressure (Minnesota, Iowa) and down in others due to odor (North Carolina).
Social	Increased efficiency helps meet an expected 20–50% higher worldwide demand over the next decade. Employment in corporate firms tends to be more culturally diverse than traditional farms, but can stress community services like schools and hospitals. There is great debate about environmental impacts. Odor, water quality from runoff and leaching, and nitrate deposition through precipitation are all concerns. Findings indicate mixed impacts from size. Animal welfare advocates are concerned with too little space, disease, and boredom.

Source: Hoag and Fathel-Rahman forthcoming

Crisis 3: Feeding a Growing World

Exhibit 14. Food and Economic Indicators of the Past and Future

Lester Brown has been called "the world's leading modern Malthusian." He sees a bleak future for the world, which is often demonstrated in his Worldwatch Institute annual book series titled *State of the World*. In this exhibit, Brown draws the conclusion that an economic era is coming to an end as it is replaced by an environmental era. The new era will see no more increases in seafood catch, and limited but falling per capita growth in grain production. Food prices will rise, and developing nations will suffer.

Indicator	Economic Era 1950–1990	Environmental Era 1990–2030
Seafood catch per person	rising	falling
Grain production per person	rising	falling
Food prices	falling	rising
Grain market	buyer's market	seller's market
Politics of food	dominated by surpluses	dominated by scarcity
Income per person	rising	may decline for much of the world

Source: Brown 1995, p. 128

Exhibit 15. Trends in World Crop Supply and Demand Growth Rates for Selected Years

This interesting estimation by Tweeten paints a comforting picture. Supply of food, he predicts, will lag behind demand until population tops out in the year 2050. In the year 2050, however, the supply of crops will rise by 0.77 percent, but demand will only increase by 0.68 percent. This will actually cause prices to fall. Tweeten bases these estimates on a linear growth rate of crop yields. Some people think productivity growth rates are slowing down because the growth rates in the last two decades have been consecutively lower than three decades ago. However, others argue that biotechnology or simply disseminating the cropping knowledge we already have can easily keep growth rates high. Tweeten's estimates assume that demand will increase for each additional person born and from higher incomes per capita. In a sensitivity analysis, Tweeten concludes that there is no reason for "panic nor complacency." Higher prices will be a hardship on the poor, but prices will not rise enough to cause alarm. We must keep investing in productivity growth, he believes, and population should not grow to a level that cannot be fed.

Supply and Demand	2000	2010	2020	2030	2040	2050
	——— (% change) per year ———					
Supply						
Cereals	1.42	1.25	1.11	1.00	0.91	0.83
Vegetables	1.06	0.95	0.87	0.80	0.74	0.69
Pulses	0.72	0.68	0.63	0.60	0.56	0.53
Roots and tubers	0.62	0.59	0.55	0.52	0.50	0.47
Oilseeds	0.41	0.40	0.38	0.37	0.35	0.34
Total (weighted average)	1.28	1.14	1.01	0.92	0.84	0.77
Demand						
Population gain[a]	1.44	1.24	1.08	0.88	0.65	0.48
Income gain	0.31	0.29	0.27	0.24	0.22	0.20
Total demand gain (population + income)	1.75	1.53	1.35	1.12	0.87	0.68
Excess demand						
Demand less yield gain	0.47	0.39	0.34	0.20	0.03	-0.09
Price impact	1.41	1.17	1.02	0.60	0.09	-0.27

a) Based on United Nations' prediction of population growth

Source: Adapted from Tweeten 1998

Crisis 4: Safe Food and Drinking Water

Exhibit 16. Mad Cow Disease (BSE) and Chronic Wasting Disease (CWD)

Mad cow disease scared many people and cost beef producers in Great Britain a lot of money. In the United States, we have our own version of the disease called chronic wasting disease in some deer and elk populations.

➤ Discovered in November 1986, bovine spongiform encephalopathy (BSE), widely referred to as "mad cow disease," is a chronic degenerative disease affecting the central nervous system of cattle.

➤ Between November 1986 and 1996, 160,000 cases were confirmed in the United Kingdom, where it seems to be concentrated.

➤ Industry profits were reduced over 25 percent and tens of thousands of animals have been slaughtered.

➤ Epidemiological studies suggested that the source of the disease was cattle feed prepared from carcasses of dead ruminants. There is no evidence that BSE spreads horizontally, i.e., by contact between unrelated adult cattle or from cattle to other species.

➤ The agent affects the brain and spinal cord of cattle and, lesions are characterized by spongelike changes visible with an ordinary microscope. The disease is fatal for cattle within weeks to months of its onset.

➤ BSE has been linked to a variant of Creutzfeldt-Jakob disease in humans when they consume neural tissue. The World Health Organization concluded that no definite link between BSE and the variant of Creutzfeldt-Jakob disease could be established. However, circumstantial evidence suggested that exposure to BSE was the most likely cause of the 10–30 cases in the United Kingdom and one in France.

➤ BSE is one of several different forms of transmissible brain disease in animals. Another is chronic wasting disease.

➤ Chronic wasting disease (CWD) is a mad cow–like disease found in deer and elk in the western United States.

Exhibit 16 (continued)

➤ No one has become sick from coming in contact with the wasting disease—but wildlife officials sometimes require hunters to turn in the heads of deer or elk they've killed, and some hunters in the infected areas are avoiding the consumption of any neural tissue.

➤ Federal and state agencies have launched three studies to determine its transmissibility to cattle. So far, officials suspect only a slight risk for animals with common calving grounds.

Source: Adapted from various sources including World Health Organization 1996

Exhibit 17. Costs of Foodborne Pathogens in the United States (1995 Dollars)

Foodborne pathogens like *E. coli* and *Salmonella* make 3 to 12 million people sick every year. Actual illnesses are likely higher because many people think they have a simple illness like the flu when they get sick from these organisms. Tragically, 2,000 to 4,000 people die from the seven most common bacteria or parasites every year. Premature deaths, treatment, productivity loss, prevention, animal losses, surveillance, research, and legal suits are estimated to cost from $6.5 billion to $34.9 billion every year.

Pathogen and Disease/Complication	Estimated Foodborne Illness Scope: Cases	Deaths	Estimated Foodborne Illness Costs Assuming Life Value: $5 Million per Life Estimate[a]	Landefeld & Seskin Estimate[b]
	Number (Estimated Annual)		Billion Dollars	
Bacteria:				
Campylobacter jejuni or coli				
Campylobacteriosis	1,100,000–7,000,000	110–622	$1.2–6.6	$0.7–4.3
Clostridium perfringens				
C. Perfringens intoxications	10,000	100	0.5	0.1
Escherichia coli O157:H7				
E. coli O157:H7 disease	8,000–16,000	80–200	0.4–1.0	0.1–0.3
Hemolytic uremic syndrome[c]	320–656	96–233	0.5–1.2	0.2–0.4
Subtotal		176–433	0.9–2.2	0.3–0.7

Listeria monocytogenes[d]			
Listeriosis	928–1,767	230–485	$1.2–2.4	$0.11–0.3
Complications	22–41	0	0.1–0.2	0.03–0.05
Subtotal		230–485	1.3–2.4	0.1–0.3
Salmonella (nontyphoid)			
Salmonellosis	696,000–3,840,000	870–1,920	4.8–12.2	0.9–3.5
Staphylococcus aureus			
S. aureus intoxications	1,513,000	454	3.3	1.2
Parasite:			
Toxoplasma gondii[e]			
Toxoplasmosis	217	40	0.1	0.04
Complications	1,541	0	7.6	3.15
Subtotal	1,581	40	7.7	3.2
Total[f]	3,300,000–12,300,000	1,900–3,900	19.7–34.9	6.5–13.3

a The $5 million value of a statistical life was estimated from wage-risk studies. Costs equal the number of people who die times $5 million.

b This human-capital approach estimates the value of a statistical life to range from $15,000 to $1,979,000 depending on the age at death (younger people have higher value since they have a longer life expectancy).

c Kidney failure.

d Includes only hospitalized patients.

e Includes only toxoplasmosis cases related to fetuses and newborn children who may become blind or mentally retarded.

f Totals are rounded down.

Source: Buzby and Roberts 1996, p. 21

Exhibit 18. A Shopper's Guide to Pesticides in Produce

The Food and Drug Administration estimates that less than 1 percent of our food is contaminated with pesticide residues. Several consumer groups feel this is too much risk. This shopper's guide implies that normally healthy foods such as strawberries and peaches are loaded with pesticides because half of all "dietary" risk is from just 12 crops. This is half of the risk on the small amount of food that is contaminated, not on half of all strawberries, peaches, or apricots.

The Environmental Working Group (EWG) obtained data from the U.S. Food and Drug Administration on the amount of pesticides in 42 fruits and vegetables. They found that more than half of the total dietary risk (human carcinogens, nervous system poisons, and endocrine system disrupters) from pesticides in these foods was concentrated in just 12 crops, ranked from worst to best below:

1	Strawberries	7	Celery
2	(tie) Bell peppers (green and red)	8	Apples
2	(tie) Spinach	9	Apricots
4	Cherries (U.S.)	10	Green beans
5	Peaches	11	Grapes (Chilean)
6	Cantaloupe (Mexican)	12	Cucumbers

Source: Environmental Working Group Web site

Exhibit 19. Relative Carcinogenic Hazards from Average U.S. Exposures (HERP Rankings)

Bruce Ames is a controversial figure for his assertion that 99.9 percent of risk in food comes from food itself rather than synthetic additives such as pesticides (Ames 1993). Ames developed the Human Exposure/Rodent Potency (HERP) rankings, which indicate the potency of specific compounds to create cancerous tumors. A HERP index of 100 percent means that the human exposure is equal to the dose—amount consumed daily (mg/kg/day) over a lifetime—that would give 50 percent of rodents tumors during their lifetimes.

An often-used government regulatory standard is that no more than one out of every 1 million people should get cancer from carcinogenic compounds that are present at levels below the "acceptable" limit. This standard converts to a HERP score of 0.00003. Another compairson is that chloroform in a liter of ordinary tap water has a HERP index of 0.00001. The chemical Alar, which was used on apples, was driven from the market due to its potential cancer-causing properties. Alar has a HERP index that is 100 times

Exhibit 19 (continued)

greater than the government standard and 333 times greater than chloroform found in tap water. The levels of aniline in carrots, d-Limonene in orange juice, and caffeic acid found in coffee, lettuce, and potatoes all have HERP rankings that are hundreds to thousands times greater than that of Alar. A single sleeping pill has a HERP 14 million times greater than the government standard. The ethyl alcohol found in a can of beer is over 200,000 times greater.

Hazard Index[a]	Item and Exposure	Carcinogen
140	1 Sleeping Pill	Phenobarbital
2.1	257 Grams of Beer	Ethyl alcohol
1.4	Mobile Home Air	Formaldehyde
0.5	28 Grams of Wine	Ethyl alcohol
0.4	Conventional Home Air	Formaldehyde
0.1	13.3 Grams of Coffee	Caffeic acid
0.04	14.9 Grams of Lettuce	Caffeic acid
0.03	138 Grams of Orange Juice	d-Limonene
0.02	13.3 Grams of Coffee	Catechol
0.02	13.3 Grams of Coffee	Furfural
0.008	Aflatoxin (1984–1989)	Aflatoxin\
0.005	Carrot (12.1 Grams)	Aniline
0.004	Potato (54.9 Grams)	Caffeic acid
0.001	Plum (2 Grams)	Caffeic acid
0.001	Alar (average exposure)	UDMH
0.0004	11.5 Grams of Bacon	N-Nitrosoyrrolidine
0.0003	1 Liter of Tap Water	Chloroform
0.0002	Alar in 1 Apple	UDMH
<0.00000001	Synthetic Pesticide Chlorothalonil	Chlorothalonil
0.000000008	Synthetic Pesticide Folpet	Folpet
0.000000006	Synthetic Pesticide Captan	Captan

a) The Human Exposure/Rodent Potency (HERP) shows, for any given dose (mg/kg/day) that a human could take over a lifetime, the comparative risk that was found in rodent studies. For example, a HERP of 100 percent would compare to the level found to give tumors to 50 percent of rodents. The typical standard of safety required by the government is no more than a one-in-a-million chance of getting cancer from something that is consumed at a given level every day over a lifetime. This safety standard translates into a HERP score of 0.00001.

Source: Ames and Gold 1997

Exhibit 20. President's National Food Safety Initiative, 1997

This initiative is a multiagency effort to strengthen and improve food safety efforts by:

➤ Improved inspections and expanded preventive safety measures. The initiative calls for increased funds for FDA inspection activities, implementation of HACCP-type (see Glossary) systems for fruit and vegetable juice industries, and proposes implementation of HACCP systems for egg products.

➤ Accelerated research to develop new tests to detect foodborne pathogens and to assess risks to the food supply.

➤ Establishment of a new early-warning surveillance system to detect and respond to outbreaks of foodborne illnesses, and to gather the data necessary to prevent future outbreaks. This system is called "FoodNet," and is administered by the Centers for Disease Control and Prevention (CDC).

➤ Establishment of a national educational campaign that will improve food handling in homes and retail outlets. This reflects the fact that prevention at the farm and processing level will probably never eliminate foodborne risks—consumers and retailers, too, have a responsibility to prepare and handle foods properly to prevent disease.

➤ Strengthening and improving coordination among federal agencies responsible for food safety, including U.S. Department of Agriculture, Center for Disease Control, Food and Drug Administration, and Environmental Protection Agency.

Source: Crutchfield et al. 1997

Exhibit 21. Texas Cattle Feeders versus Oprah Winfrey

After the National Resources Defense Council's report on Alar hurt the apple industry, many states passed so called "veggie libel" laws to protect farmers and ranchers from false or careless claims. The first real test of these laws saw defeat as Oprah Winfrey beat Texas cattle producers that sued her for comments on her show.

➤ After the incident over the chemical Alar used in the apple industry reduced grower incomes by as much as $100 million in 1989, 13 states passed legislation prohibiting certain negative remarks about food products. These "veggie libel" laws gave food producers the right to sue an accuser if they could prove a false statement was made with malice or intent to harm, or that the statement induced others not to purchase or carry the agricultural product.

➤ The veggie laws were created out of a feeling of unfairness because someone who claimed a product was harmful was not responsible for losses if their claims were false or misleading. These laws did not hold up well, however, when put to the test when Texas Beef Group, led by Paul Engler of Cactus Feeders, sued Oprah Winfrey et al. for remarks made on one of her television talk shows. Howard Lyman, director of the American Humane Society's "Eating with Conscience" campaign, said on the show that cows were being fed the carcasses of other cows that had died in the feedlots. He also claimed that mad cow disease could easily be spread to thousands of people through meat from infected cows. Finally, he said that mad cow disease could make "AIDS look like the common cold." Oprah responded "It has just stopped me cold from eating another burger."

➤ The information, the plaintiffs claimed, caused Engler's cattle company to lose about $7 million. Another $3–$5 million was lost by coplaintiffs. Engler argued that the statements made on Winfrey's show were false and led to an immediate drop of $1.50 per hundredweight in the futures market on the day of the show alone. Witnesses for the defense acknowledged that there could have been some impact but found that the plaintiffs had exaggerated their claim.

➤ The jury found that the defendant did not publish a false, disparaging statement about the cattle industry. In cases like these, it is difficult to prove one way or the other what is true and untrue, so people like Lyman can make statements that are disparaging as long as they believe them to be true (within reason). In addition, it was highly likely that damages would have been hard to prove as well, if the jury had found differently. Currently, over 130 feeders have filed new suits and Engler's group has vowed to appeal.

Source: Hayenga 1998

Exhibit 22. Risks Estimated to Increase the Chance of Death by One in a Million (Government Regulatory Level)

The government is responsible for keeping our food safe. Zero tolerance is not seen as realistic or desirable by most people because we take risks every day when we think that the benefits outweigh the costs. This table shows many everyday activities that carry an estimated one-in-a-million risk of death in a year. The government generally will not allow a food product on the market if it presents a one-in-a-million chance of any adverse health effect.

Activity	Cause of Death
Smoking 1.4 cigarettes	Cancer, heart disease
Spending 1 hour in a coal mine	Black lung disease
Living 60 days in a brick house	Cancer from natural radiation
Traveling 10 minutes on a bike	Accident
Flying 1,000 miles by jet	Accident
Flying 6,000 miles by jet	Cancer from cosmic radiation
120 minutes of sailing	Accident
6 minutes in a canoe	Accident
43 minutes on a school bus	Accident
One chest x-ray	Cancer from radiation
Eating 40 tablespoons of peanut butter	Liver cancer from aflatoxin
100 flame-broiled steaks	Cancer from benzopyrene
Living 150 years within 20 miles of a nuclear power plant	Cancer from radiation
Living 2 months in Denver	Cancer from cosmic radiation
Living 2 days in New York or Boston	Air pollution
Living 20 minutes at the age of 60	Natural causes

Various sources

Exhibit 23. Costs and Benefits of HACCP Pathogen Reduction Rules

Since foodborne illnesses are so common in the United States, the government initiated a set of policies designed to reduce our risk of exposure associated with processing. The process is called Hazard Analysis of Critical Control Points (HACCP). The costs of HACCP are estimated at $1.1 to $2.3 billion per year. The benefits, however, range from $1.9 to $171.8 billion. The authors of this table varied their estimates of costs and benefits to the low end by assuming only a 20 percent pathogen reduction and a high discount rate on future earnings (giving a person a lower lifetime earning potential) and by using a conservative method to estimate the value of a lost life. Their high estimate assumes a 90 percent reduction in pathogens, a low discount on future income, and the "maximum" value of a life lost.

Assumptions	Description of Assumptions	Benefits (billion $)	Costs (billion $)
Low-range	20% pathogen reduction 7% discount rate Landefeld/Seskin value of life[a]	1.9–9.3	1.1–2.3
Mid-range	50% pathogen reduction 3–7% discount rate Landefeld/Seskin value of life[a] $5 million value of life[b]	4.7–95.4	1.1–2.3
High-range	90% pathogen reduction 3% discount rate $5 million value of life[b]	47.2–171.8	1.1–2.3

a) This human-capital approach estimates the value of a statistical life to range from $15,000 to $1,979,000.
b) The $5 million value of a statistical life was estimated from wage-risk studies.

Source: Adapted from Crutchfield et al. 1997

Exhibit 24. Economic Impacts from Pesticide Restriction in the United States from Various Studies

Although pesticides cause environmental problems and threaten human health, we get benefits from them, too. Many economists have estimated the costs of partially or fully reducing pesticide use. These costs could be weighed against the benefits that society would enjoy if pesticides were not used. For example, in 1990, Knutson et al. estimated that banning all pesticides on eight crops would cost consumers $18 billion per year.

Authors (Year)	Regulatory Scenario	Economic or Agricultural Impact
Chambers and Lichtenberg (1994)	Aggregate effects of no pesticides	Maximum 20 percent damage to all crops
Ferguson and Padula (1994)	Ban of methyl bromide	$1 billion/year farm and consumer costs
Gianessi and Anderson (1995)	Zero tolerance via Delaney clause	$387 million new costs to farmers
Helmers, Azzam, and Spilder (1990)	10% reduction in chemical inputs	1.6% reduction in wheat yield 2.2% reduction in soybeans
Knutson et al. (1990)	Total ban on all pesticides on 8 crops	Severe yield reductions $18 billion consumer loss
Knutson et al. (1993)	Total ban on all pesticides for 9 fruits and vegetables	Severe yield reductions Whole state industries wiped out
Olsen, Langley, and Heady (1982)	Widespread adoption of organic farming	National net farm income and consumer costs increase; exports fall
Pimental et al. (1991)	50% reduction in pesticide use	$1 billion in farmers' costs
Taylor (1995)	Total ban on pesticides in fruit and vegetable production and processing	Retail prices increase by 27% Farm returns fall by 30%
Zilberman et al. (1991)	Effect of California's Big Green proposition on 5 crops	Total economic harm to producers and consumers $0.9–$1.75 billion

Source: Adapted from Jaenicke 1997

Exhibit 25. Effort and Cost of Pesticide Approval

One industry defense about pesticides is the tremendous cost and effort that are required for a product to get to market. This effort and cost to assure safety and benefit make it unlikely that harmful products will make it to market.

➤ On average, only 1 in 20,000 chemicals make it from the laboratory to the marketplace.

➤ Before a chemical meets all health and environmental approvals, it is subjected to 120 separate tests.

➤ To develop, test, and receive EPA approval for a new pesticide, manufacturers spend eight to ten years and $35 to $50 million.

Source: The National Agricultural Chemicals Association

Crisis 5: Stewardship and the Environment

Exhibit 26. Environmental Costs Relative to Value of Crops Produced (1984)

Smith estimated that for every dollar of commodity sold, there is almost 5 cents damage to the environment from soil erosion, nearly another 2 cents to wetlands, and another 6 cents to groundwater from contamination. He estimates that in total, counting only these costs, there is almost 13 cents of damage to the environment for every dollar of commodity sold. We all benefit from lower prices and suffer from environmental costs. The question is, how much efficiency are we willing to trade off for a clean, healthy environment? Smith also computed costs by region. The highest potential cost was in the Northwest, at 40 cents. The lowest potential costs were in the mountain states.

(Exhibit continues on next page.)

Exhibit 26 (continued)

	Best	Low	High
		percent of total ag sales	
Soil Erosion (by resource)			
Freshwater recreation	0.47	0.19	1.47
Marine recreation	0.13	0.10	0.53
Water storage	0.25	0.15	0.34
Navigation	0.17	0.12	0.21
Flooding	0.22	0.15	0.35
Irrigation and related ditches	0.15	0.07	0.22
Commercial fishing	0.10	0.09	0.14
Municipal water treatment	0.22	0.11	0.32
Municipal and industrial use	0.27	0.15	1.13
Total	1.98	1.13	4.71
Mean (across states)	4.57	2.81	9.20
Wetlands Conversion Losses			
Coastal	0.36[a]	0.32[b]	6.43[b]
All other	1.54[a]	1.41[b]	4.81[b]
Groundwater Contamination			
Mean (across states)	6.27	2.58	37.49

Aggregate by Crop-Production Region

Northeast	3.45–40.27
Appalachia	7.15–13.03
Southeast	6.71–14.40
Lake States	6.95–11.86
Corn Belt	5.60–7.39
Delta States	7.90–11.10
Northern Plains	2.70–4.30
Southern Plains	4.64–4.68
Mountain	0.08–7.49
Pacific	4.91–6.25
Total Cost[c]	12.74

a) functional value
b) total value
c) sum of best for soil erosion, wetlands, and groundwater

Source: Adapted from Smith 1992

Exhibit 27. Commercial Fertilizer Use, 1960–1995

Except for nitrogen, fertilizer levels have remained relatively steady for the last 40 years.

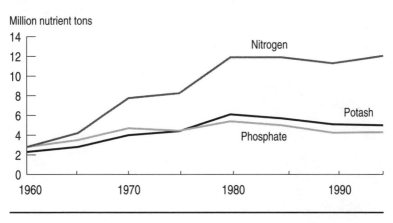

Source: USDA 1997

Exhibit 28. Overall Pesticide Use on Selected U.S. Crops, 1966–1995

Pesticide use has also remained amazingly constant, except for herbicides, which have increased by 200–300 percent.

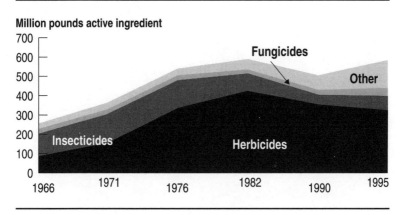

Source: USDA 1997

Exhibit 29. National Use of Conservation Tillage, 1996

One of the most touted environmental practices a farmer can use is conservation (no tillage, minimal tillage, etc.) or ridge tillage. It saves fuel and labor and leaves protective residue that prevents soil erosion. In 1996, almost two-thirds of all cropland used conservation or reduced tillage.

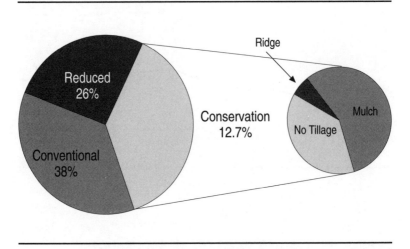

Source: USDA 1997

Exhibit 30. Survey Results of Water Impaired by Agriculture

The U.S. EPA requires that states collect information about water pollution. While lakes and rivers have improved, agriculture still accounts for the largest share of "impairments."

➤ Nationally, states assessed 18% of river and stream miles, 46% of lake acres, and 74% of estuary square miles.

- Rivers and streams: 38% of assessed miles were impaired; 72% of these were affected by agricultural pollution.

- Lakes: 44% of assessed acres were impaired; 56% of these were affected by agricultural nonpoint pollution.

- Estuaries: 32% of assessed square miles were impaired; 43% of these were affected by agricultural pollution.

➤ A 1990 national survey of drinking-water wells by the U.S. EPA found:

- 10% of the nation's community drinking wells and about 4% of the rural domestic wells have detectable residues of at least one pesticide.

- Less than 1% of wells had pesticide residues above the levels considered protective of human health.

- One-half of the nation's wells contained nitrate, with about 1.2% of community wells and 2.4% of rural wells showing detections above the 10-ppm level set to protect human health.

➤ All states except Alaska, South Dakota, and Wyoming issued fish consumption advisories in 1994 due to harmful toxic pollutants.

➤ Over 6,000 square miles of shellfish beds in 15 states were closed between 1992 and 1994.

➤ There were over 1,454 fish-kill incidents from 1992 to 1993, blamed mainly on pesticides and manure.

➤ Sediments in water cost $2 billion in 1989, but have trended downward throughout the 1980s.

Various sources including USDA 1997

Exhibit 31. Trends in Agricultural Pollutant Concentrations in Surface Water, 1980–1990

Water Resources Region	Nitrate	Phosphorus	Suspended Sediment
		(Average percent change per year)	
North Atlantic		-1.4	-0.4
South Atlantic–Gulf		0.1	0.2
Great Lakes		-3.3	-0.5
Ohio–Tennessee		-1.0	-1.3
Upper Mississippi	-0.4	-1.2	-1.3
Lower Mississippi	-1.6	-3.8	-1.2
Souris–Red–Rainy		-0.8	-1.2
Missouri		-1.7	-0.2
Arkansas–White–Red		-3.1	-0.7
Texas–Gulf–Rio Grande		-0.9	-0.6
Colorado		-2.4	-0.8
Great Basin		-2.7	-0.2
Pacific Northwest		-1.7	-0.1
California		-1.4	-0.6

Source: USDA 1997

Exhibit 32. The Natural Values and Services from a Wetland

How do economists estimate the value of something not sold in the market? This example for a wetland shows that many impacts are included.

I. Intermediate Goods and Services (serve as factors of production for other goods)

A. Commercial factors (serve as factors of production for market goods)
- Support of commercial fisheries
- Provision of commercially harvested natural resources (timber, peat)
- Water supply and storage
- Assimilation of wastes (for tertiary treatment of human wastes)

B. Damage prevention factors (serve as factors of production for a wide variety of goods and services)
- Pollution assimilation/water purification
- Flood control
- Erosion prevention

II. Final Goods and Services (produce consumer satisfaction directly)

A. Recreational opportunities
- Consumptive uses (fishing, hunting)
- Nonconsumptive uses (camping, hiking, boating, bird-watching)

B. Amenities
- Scenic value
- Spiritual value
- Education

III. Future Goods and Services (may fall into any of the categories above)

A. Undiscovered goods

B. Future high-value development

Source: Scodari 1990

Exhibit 33. Simulated Impacts of Global Climate Change on Developed and Developing Countries in the Year 2060

Global climate change is a hot topic, but is it really a bad thing? Fischer et al. estimated the impacts of climate change on agriculture based on several studies. Three of four studies showed that world food production and agricultural income would actually rise due to climate change. Plants like the extra CO_2. However, an equally important point is that the gap between rich and poor nations will grow because developing nations will lose and developed nations will gain. Does the distributional impact outweigh the gain in efficiency?

	Crop Production in 2060[a] % Change			Agriculture GDP % Change[c]
	GISS[b]	GFDL[b]	UKMO[b]	
World Total	3.2	1.0	-4.4	0.0
Developed Nations	13.1	6.4	-0.8	6.5
Developing Nations	-0.1	-0.8	-5.6	-2.2

a) Assumes that plants will gain physiological benefits of CO_2 and that farmers will adapt farming practices to new weather conditions.
b) GISS is Goddard Institute for Space Studies, GFDL is Geophysical Fluid Dynamics Laboratory, and UKMO is United Kingdom Meteorological Office circulation. Models used an assumed doubling of CO_2 emissions.
c) Assumes economic adjustments in world prices and likewise in farm practices are made in reaction to changing climate. That is, as the climate shifts, producers change their farming practices to reduce negative impacts, for example, by changing to a drought-resistant crop.

Source: Fischer et al. 1994

Exhibit 34. Economic Value Estimates for Rare, Threatened, and Endangered Species[a]

Loomis and White looked at hundreds of studies to determine the value of endangered species. The studies that they used computed the value of an endangered species through complex techniques that determine the economic value of nonmarket goods. Relatively unknown species like the striped shiner were worth about $6 per person per year, while a popular species like the bald eagle was worth $24 per person per year.

SPECIES	Low Estimate	High Estimate	Average of All Studies
Results for annual payments			
Northern spotted owl	44	95	70
Pacific salmon/Steelhead	31	88	63
Grizzly bear			46
Whooping crane			35
Red-cockaded woodpecker	10	15	13
Sea otter			29
Gray whale	17	33	26
Bald eagle	15	33	24
Bighorn sheep	12	30	21
Sea turtle			13
Atlantic salmon	7	8	8
Squawfish			8
Striped shiner			6
Results for a onetime lump sum			
Monk seal			120
Gray wolf	16	118	67
Arctic grayling/Cutthroat trout	13	17	15
Bald eagles	178	254	216
Humpback whale			173

a) Statistical estimation of value based on published studies.
Note: Blank cells indicate that estimates were unavailable.

Source: Adapted from Loomis and White 1996

Exhibit 35. Types of Environmental Consumers in the United States

When it comes to the environment, many people talk the talk, but do they put their money where their mouth is? This interesting survey by the Food Marketing Institute shows that about half of the consumers in the United States use environmental considerations in their purchases. In addition, over 60 percent of these buyers are inconsistent in their environmental habits. For example, 12 percent are "affluent healers" that are concerned, but altruistic and generally more concerned about food quality than the environment.

True Naturals *(7% of U.S. population)*
Commitment to environmentally sound products as a part of their lifestyles. Most knowledgeable about environmental food issues and like to learn more. Self-sufficient and secure. Status and style conscious. Represent the core market for organic and natural foods. Most likely to shop in health/natural food stores.

Young Recyclers *(10% of U.S. population)*
Concerned about environmental issues, but concern does not always translate into action. Very sensitive to packaging and recycling issues. Not willing to pay price premiums for environmentally friendly products. Concerned about nutrition but less likely to eat healthy. Favor convenience foods. Feel self-sufficient. Identify with pop culture.

New Green Mainstream *(23% of U.S. population)*
High level of concern for the environment, but inconsistent in expressing this concern through purchase decisions. Don't feel knowledgeable about food-related environmental issues. Interested in learning about environmental food issues to make informed purchase decisions. Tend to be altruistic. Interested in trying new things.

Affluent Healers *(12% of U.S. population)*
Environmentally concerned, but less than other green segments. The well-being of their family is extremely important. Strong work ethic. Thrifty. Altruistic. Generally willing to pay more for high-quality products, but not for environmentally improved products.

Source: Food Marketing Institute 1997

Exhibit 36. Green Consumer Habits Survey

The Food Marketing Institute also looked at buying habits. Pesticide residue, fertilizer use, or soil conservation influence the buying habits of less than half the population. Only 25 percent say they are very interested in purchasing environmentally friendly products; this drops to 8 percent if they have to pay 10 percent more. Only about 15 percent have purchased an environmentally friendly product in the last month, and about half that have purchased organic products.

	Total Population	True Naturals	New Green Mainstream	Young Recyclers	Affluent Healers
Influence on Grocery Shopping					
Water protection	59	80	78	74	63
Absence of pesticide residues on food	47	72	71	53	55
Use of natural fertilizers	37	72	58	45	40
Limited use of pesticides	35	71	57	38	38
Use of beneficial insects	33	63	55	40	33
Soil conservation	32	63	47	40	34
Elimination of pesticide use	32	63	57	31	30
Interest in Environmentally Enhanced Products					
Very interested in purchasing environmentally enhanced products	25	67	43	25	19
Very interested in purchasing environmentally enhanced products priced 10% higher	8	38	16	6	4
Purchase of Environmentally Friendly Products in Last Month					
Fresh produce	16	47	20	17	10
Dairy (milk, eggs, butter)	15	37	17	16	10
Meat/poultry	11	31	11	12	7
Purchase of Organic Products in Last Month					
Fresh produce	7	32	11	5	3
Dairy (milk, eggs, butter)	4	15	5	3	2
Meat/poultry	3	1	4	3	1

Source: Adapted from Food Marketing Institute 1997

Exhibit 37. Government Resource Conservation Program Expenditures Affecting Agriculture, 1996

The U.S. government spent nearly $7 billion on conservation-related programs for agriculture in 1997. The lion's share is spent by USDA.

Agency and Program	Expenditures ($ Million)
U.S. Department of Agriculture (USDA)	
Conservation Reserve Program (CRP)	1,782
Wetlands Programs	72
Water Quality Program	193
Other Conservation Programs	1,153
Total	3,200
U.S. Environmental Protection Agency (EPA)	
Water Quality Programs	526
Drinking Water Programs	184
Pesticide Programs	109
Total	819
Army Corps of Engineers Programs (ACE)	
Dredge and Fill Permit Program (wetlands)	101
Flood Control Programs	1,252
Total	1,353
U.S. Department of Interior Programs (USDI)	
Range Improvement	10
Water Development and Management	982
Water Resources Investigations	186
Wetlands Conservation	7
Endangered Species Conservation	36
Natural Resources Research	148
Total	1,369
Federal Total	6,741
State and Local Expenditures on USDA Programs	736
Total	7,477

Source: USDA 1997

Exhibit 38. U.S. Conservation Reserve Program (CRP) Highlights

The Conservation Reserve Program is the largest single conservation effort for agriculture in this country's history. CRP shares the cost of establishing a permanent vegetative cover (e.g., grass or trees) on highly erodible land and pays the producer an annual rental payment to keep that land out of production for ten years. Over 36 million acres of cropland were taken out of production for at least ten years, preventing an estimated 700 million tons of soil erosion per year. The government spent nearly $1.4 billion to help share the costs of establishing conservation cover and about $18 billion on annual rental payments. Producers received an average of $56 per acre for rental payments and about $3,665 per farm in cost-share payments for establishing conservation cover.

Characteristic	Value
Enrollment on Farms	
Highly Erodible Land	35.5 million acres
Wetland	0.40 million acres
Scour Land	0.14 million acres
Hydrologic Units	0.06 million acres
Conservation Priority	0.37 million acres
Total	36.6 million acres[a]
Government Costs of Contracts	
Rental Payments	$18,135,198,000
Cost Share	$1,375,440,000
Total	$19,510,638,000
Rental Payments to Farmers Nationwide	
Maximum Rent	$200/acre
Minimum Rent	$4/acre
Average Rent	$56/acre
Cost-Share Payment per Farm	$3,665
Size of Contracts (U.S. Average)	100 acres
Erosion Reduction	
Erosion before CRP (Enrolled Acres)	20.6 tons/acre/year
Erosion after CRP	1.56 tons/acre/year
Soil Saved/Year	700 million tons/year

a) Differs from apparent sum due to rounding errors.

Source: USDA

Exhibit 39. Estimated Present Value of CRP Costs and Benefits in 1990 Dollars

Granted, CRP saved a lot of soil erosion. But was it worth it? The net benefit of the program is estimated to be from -$0.3 to $8.1 billion in 1990 dollars. Therefore, the program most likely produced more benefits than it cost. Some people feel that the program was not a good investment, however, since the benefits were largely a transfer from consumers and taxpayers to producers. Most people never shared in the benefits of increased wildlife, for example.

Net Social Benefits (billions)		Net Social Costs (billions)	
Increases in net farm income	$2.1–$6.3	Higher food costs	$2.9–$7.8
		Cover establishment costs	$2.4
Future timber harvests	$3.3	Technical assistance	$0.1
Preservation of soil productivity	$0.6–$1.7	Net rental payment costs	$6.6–$9.3
Surface water quality	$1.3–$4.2		
Windblown dust damage	$0.3–$0.9		
Small-game hunting	$1.9–$3.1		
Waterfowl hunting	$1.4		
Nonconsumptive wildlife uses	$4.1		
Subtotal	$15–$25	Subtotal	$12–$20.1

Net Benefit Range[a]: High = $8.1   Low = - $0.3

a) Lows of farm income and higher food costs match high of net rental payments and visa versa.

Source: Hoag forthcoming

Exhibit 40. Estimated Benefits and Costs of Conservation Compliance by Region

Conservation compliance was required beginning in 1985. Farmers that receive financial payments from the government are required to conserve soil in highly erodible fields in return. This program saved an estimated $2 for every $1 it cost.

Region	Per-acre benefits from:			Per-acre costs to:		Net Economic Benefit	Benefit/Cost Ratio
	Water Quality	Air Quality	Productivity	Producers	Federal Gov't		
	Annual 1993 dollars per acre						
Northeast	35.63	0.00	0.16	3.57	3.43	28.80	5.12
Lake states	21.99	0.00	0.12	0.32	3.43	18.37	5.90
Corn belt	15.61	0.00	0.25	8.90	3.43	3.53	1.29
Northern plains	3.47	3.00	0.19	3.35	3.43	-0.11	0.98
Appalachia	23.58	0.00	0.24	3.51	3.43	16.89	3.43
Southeast	25.63	0.00	0.12	8.18	3.43	14.15	2.22
Delta	35.50	0.00	0.12	1.97	3.43	30.22	6.60
Southern plains	5.26	4.63	0.33	2.34	3.43	4.45	1.77
Mountain	5.10	4.01	0.15	0.20	3.43	5.63	2.55
Pacific	31.83	1.09	0.14	2.23	3.43	27.40	5.85
United States	13.81	1.93	0.21	3.78	3.43	8.74	2.21

Source: Hoag forthcoming

Crisis 6: Urbanization and Land Use

Exhibit 41. States Ranked by Acreage of Prime or Unique Farmland Converted to Urban (1982–1992)

The state rankings of prime and unique farmland conversion to urban uses between 1982 and 1992 are shown in this table. In Wyoming, less than 1 percent was converted. In Iowa, conversion topped 100 percent because some land was converted more than once. On average, about 31 percent of prime and unique (i.e., historically significant) farmland was converted over this period.

State	Prime/Unique Farmland Converted	Total Land Developed	Percent Prime/Unique Developed[a]	Percent Prime/Unique Land[a]
TX	489,000	1,402,000	35	22
NC	295,000	941,000	31	22
OH	281,000	472,000	59	45
GA	183,000	760,000	24	22
LA	177,000	270,000	66	41
FL	166,000	1,193,000	14	7
IL	165,000	240,000	69	59
TN	159,000	436,000	36	24
IN	147,000	229,000	64	58
CA	146,000	800,000	18	12
MI	142,000	463,000	31	23
PA	141,000	436,000	32	15
VA	134,000	440,000	30	20
KY	127,000	368,000	35	23
WI	113,000	249,000	45	27
AL	106,000	324,000	33	23
SC	101,000	408,000	25	18
NJ	98,000	298,000	33	16
MN	97,000	240,000	41	41
AZ	80,000	365,000	22	2
NY	74,000	222,000	33	15
OK	72,000	158,000	46	33

Exhibit 41 (continued)

State	Prime/Unique Farmland Converted	Total Land Developed	Percent Prime/Unique Developed	Percent Prime/Unique Land
KS	72,000	123,000	59	45
MS	66,000	144,000	45	36
OR	61,000	164,000	37	12
MO	60,000	204,000	29	34
WA	59,000	288,000	21	8
IA	50,000	50,000	101[b]	52
MD	43,000	149,000	29	19
ND	42,000	107,000	40	27
ID	42,000	94,000	44	17
AR	37,000	97,000	38	42
MA	35,000	233,000	15	7
CO	32,000	309,000	10	4
NE	27,000	38,000	71	25
UT	24,000	108,000	22	5
CT	19,000	84,000	22	10
SD	17,000	64,000	27	14
DE	17,000	35,000	48	33
WV	16,000	115,000	14	4
ME	14,000	98,000	14	5
MT	8,000	82,000	10	1
NH	8,000	152,000	5	3
VT	8,000	65,000	12	6
RI	7,000	26,000	25	9
NM	6,000	162,000	4	1
NV	4,000	83,000	5	3
WY	1,000	40,000	3	1
US Total	4,266	13,823	31	—

a) Figures rounded to nearest whole number
b) Figure exceeds 100% because some land was converted and reconverted.

Source: Adapted from Sorensen, Greene, and Russ 1997

Exhibit 42. Key Factors of Conversion of Undeveloped Land or Sprawl

Why is farmland being lost to urbanization? Population growth is the most obvious answer, but increasing dependence on cars, more telecommuting, and poor tax planning (businesses move from cities to rural areas to take advantage of lower taxes), to name a few, are also important.

1. Increasing population and number of households

2. Migration from urban centers to newer suburban housing

3. New suburban housing on large lots

4. Commercial developments in suburban areas: shopping malls and office parks

5. Golf courses

6. Increasing dependence on the automobile: more vehicle miles traveled, more cars per family, and new road construction

7. Increased telecommuting

8. Isolation of communities in the inner cities and old suburbs

9. Lack of regional planning or tax-base sharing

10. Perception that new suburbs are safer

11. Perception that suburbs have lower costs for businesses because of property tax incentives to attract more tax base

12. Perception that suburbs have lower home ownership costs

Source: Adapted from Daniels and Bowers 1997

Exhibit 43. Values Related to Opens Spaces on Ranches

People say they value open spaces and ranches. This study confirms it. Over 40 percent of survey respondents said they would pay $125 per year to protect open space. Another 20 percent would pay at least $30.

Value	Details	Result
Contribution to Enjoyment of Living in the Country (mean score: based on a 9-point total)	*Natural Environment:* mountains, forests, rivers, climate, waterfalls	8.17
	Ranch Open Space: birds, wildflowers, grazing livestock, hay stacks, cowboys, corrals, and ranch buildings	7.77
	Western Ranch Culture: clothing, art, furniture, riding equipment, history, food, music, speech pattern	6.02
	Recreation Investments: trails, campgrounds, swimming pools, golf	5.92
	Urban Development: historic buildings, theater, restaurants, condos	5.29
Reason for Protecting Ranch Open Space (percent indicating reason as their first choice; the other category is omitted)	*Actual Direct Use:* actually viewing open space	19.7 %
	Bequest: Knowing that future generations can enjoy	12.0 %
	Existence: Knowing that ranch/open space exists for its own sake (soil conservation, water and wildlife protection, historic preservation)	27.1 %
	Option: retain opportunity to enjoy later	9.2 %
	Private Local Economy: knowing that ranchland is protected for private enterprise as part of local economy	29.5 %

(Exhibit continues on next page)

Exhibit 43 (continued)

Value	Details	Result
Willingness to Pay to Protect Open Space (per year payment to protect)	zero	7.6 %
	$20 or less	19.3 %
	$30–$50	19.2 %
	$60–$100	26.4 %
	$125–$300	15.8 %
	$400 or more	11.7 %
Preferred Protection Approaches (based on percentage of people that had a positive preference toward a protection approach)	Purchase and lease back	45.2 %
	Purchase for recreation	45.9 %
	Purchase for development rights	61.1 %
	Zoning and regulations	69.4 %
	Purchase with lottery fund	64.3 %
	Market allocation	42.1 %
	Other	10.8 %

Source: Details gathered from Rosenberger, Walsh, and McKean 1996

Exhibit 44. Selected Land Protection Tools

Many organizations and communities are working hard to figure out how to preserve open spaces and agricultural land. This exhibit summarizes some of the most common. A list of land protection terms can also be found in the Glossary.

Generally enacted at the state level

Agricultural District Laws—Special allowances for agriculture in a defined region, such as preferential taxes, protection from annexation, and right-to-farm. Used in 16 states.

Conservation Easements (Purchase Development Rights)—Used in every state, grants right to use land for farming, ranching, or designated use only. Approved agent purchases right; landowners can still transfer property with easement in tact.

State Growth Management Laws—Control timing and phasing of urban growth and types of land use. Six states use for agricultural land. Oregon has protected 16 million acres since 1972.

Right-to-Farm Laws—Designed to protect farmers and ranchers from nuisance suits such as odor, noise, and dust. Every state has at least one.

Tax Relief—There are many forms of tax relief such as tax credits or reduced rates for agriculture.

Generally enacted at the local level

Agricultural Zoning—Zoning laws can be changed in many ways to protect agricultural land, including lot size restrictions, development density restrictions, and cluster zoning.

Cluster Zoning—Allows higher-density development in exchange for open land. Grouping in small sections saves open space, minimizes development area, and reduces the costs of utilities.

Transfer Development Rights—Shifts development patterns by granting concessions on one land parcel for preserving another.

Federal level

Endangered Species Act of 1973, Clean Water Act of 1970, and Coastal Zone Management Act of 1972, and the most recent farm bills (i.e., 1996 Federal Agricultural Improvement and Reform Act) all provide for the protection of environment from agriculture, which indirectly affects farmland retention.

The 1956 Interstate Highway Act provided roads that better enabled people to remain in the countryside.

Various sources: For more information see the American Farmland Trust Web site

Crisis 7: Country and Urban Conflicts

Exhibit 45. Findings of Court Cases on Takings

Society increasingly asks individuals for more "social" responsibility on their private property. For example, we ask private landowners to protect the habitat of and not to disturb endangered species on their land. When society goes too far and violates private rights, it is called a "taking." It is very difficult to tell how far is too far. For example, is it a taking to require a hog farmer to control odor when he or she was farming before the neighbors moved in? Pease summarizes recent court cases in this exhibit.

It is difficult to know when the government goes too far in taking one person's rights away to help another. The courts are not always consistent, but a consistent policy is emerging as explained below:

➤ A taking can occur if a regulation goes too far, that is, does not substantially advance a public purpose or leave an owner with reasonable economic use on the property.

➤ A taking may be found when a landowner is forced to allow public access to private property.

➤ A taking may occur when there is no direct connection between the impacts of the project and the exactions required by the government. (Exactions are requirements from the land user to help offset costs to taxpayers of public facilities, such as requiring someone building a beach house to grant public access to the beach.)

➤ The whole property must be considered. A loss on one parcel does not lead to a taking if the remainder maintains a reasonable value.

➤ A reduction in value does not necessarily constitute a taking.

➤ A regulation must be based on a valid public purpose: public health, safety, and welfare. Protection of the environment is considered public welfare.

Source: Summarized from Pease 1998

Exhibit 46. Larimer County, Colorado, Right-to-Farm Policy, 1998 (Executive Summary)

Many counties or other municipalities are trying to protect farmers by defining reasonable behavior. This is one example of a right-to-farm policy.

In July 1998 the Agricultural Advisory Board, a county-appointed citizen volunteer group, created and adopted a Right to Farm and Ranch Resolution/Policy for Larimer County. The Board of County Commissioners (BOCC) considers adoption of this resolution on September 2, 1998. The Agricultural Advisory Board (AAB) would like the BOCC to determine that it is desirable and beneficial to the citizens of Larimer County to establish and adopt by resolution a Right to Farm and Ranch Policy involving the elements of protection of agricultural operations; education of property owners and visitors; and resolution of disputes. The AAB believes such a policy would serve and promote the public health, safety, and welfare of the citizens of Larimer County.

Reasons behind Resolution:
Larimer County is changing. Population increases affect many things including development in areas that have remained rural for decades. When non-agricultural residents move into traditionally agricultural areas conflict can occur. Larimer County has a viable economic and cultural agricultural history. When agricultural operators and residents, non-agricultural residents, and visitors collide, the economic viability of agricultural operations may become threatened.

Examples of Conflicts Include:
harassment of livestock
free-roaming dogs threatening livestock
trespass by humans and livestock
livestock on roadways
gates left open
fence construction and maintenance
maintenance of ditches across private property
storm-water management
burning of ditches
complaints about noise, dust, and odor
disposal of dead animals
weeds, pest control, and chemical applications

(Exhibit continues on next page)

Exhibit 46 (continued)

In developing the Right to Farm and Ranch Policy (RTFR), the Agricultural Advisory Board:

- Believes it is important to protect agricultural operators from complaints concerning operations that are legal and responsible.
- Believes it is important to educate the public and non-agricultural residents and visitors to Larimer County about the existence, validity, and importance of the County's agricultural operations and activities.
- Believes it is important that the Board of County Commissioners (BOCC) provides a forum for the informal and non-binding resolution of disputes between agricultural operators and non-agricultural residents and visitors to Larimer County.

Upon adoption of the RTFR Policy, the Agricultural Advisory is asking the BOCC to attempt to:

- Conserve, enhance, and encourage ranching, farming, and all manner of agricultural activities and operations within and throughout Larimer County where appropriate.
- Minimize potential conflicts between agricultural and non-agricultural users of land in the County.
- Educate new rural residents and long-time agricultural operators alike to their rights, responsibilities, and obligations relating to agricultural activities.
- Integrate planning efforts to provide for the retention of traditional and important agricultural lands in agricultural production as well as the opportunity for reasonable residential and other development.

Upon adoption of the RTFR Policy, the BOCC agrees that:
It is the policy of the Board of County Commissioners of Larimer County that ranching, farming, and all manner of agricultural activities and operations within and throughout Larimer County are integral elements of and necessary for the continued vitality of the County's history, economy, landscape, open space, lifestyle, and culture. Given their importance to Larimer County, Northern Colorado, and the State, agricultural lands and operations are worthy of recognition and protection. Because, by law, Colorado is a "Right-to-Farm" State, residents and visitors must be prepared to accept the activities, sights, sounds, and smells of Larimer County's agricultural operations as a normal and necessary aspect of living in a County with a strong rural character and a healthy agricultural sector.

People with urban expectations may perceive agricultural activities, sights, sounds, and smells as inconvenient, an eyesore, or unpleasant; however, State

Exhibit 46 (continued)

law and County policy provide that ranching, farming, or other agricultural activities and operations within Larimer County shall not be considered to be nuisances so long as operated in conformance with the law and in a non-negligent manner. Residents and visitors must be prepared to encounter noises, odors, lights, mud, dust, smoke, chemicals, machinery, and livestock on public roads, storage and disposal of manure, and the application of chemical fertilizers, soil amendments, herbicides, and pesticides, by spraying and other mechanisms.

All landowners, whether agricultural business, farm, ranch, or residence, have obligations under State law and County regulation. For example they must maintain fences and adhere to open range laws which say livestock must be fenced out. Irrigators have the right to maintain irrigation ditches through established easements that transport water for their use. Irrigation ditches are not to be used for the dumping of refuse. Landowners are responsible for controlling weeds, keeping pets under control, using property in accordance with zoning, maintaining the environmental resources of the property wisely.

Residents and visitors are encouraged to learn about these rights and responsibilities and act as good neighbors and citizens of Larimer County. The Board of County Commissioners shall establish a dispute resolution procedure with mediators to informally resolve conflicts that may arise between landowners or residents relating to agricultural operations or activities. When rural residents cannot come to an agreement or understanding about fences, ditches, livestock, or other agricultural issues, this may be the forum used to resolve disputes. Mediators must be knowledgeable, solution oriented, and at least one such mediator in each dispute must be directly involved in agriculture or an agricultural producer must serve in an advisory role to the trained mediator.

The Board, with the primary assistance of the Colorado State University Cooperative Extension Larimer County Office and through the use of County Staff as needed, shall support efforts to educate and inform the public of the Right to Farm and Ranch Policy by developing a public education and information campaign. Children and adults are exposed to different hazards in rural areas than they are in urban or suburban setting. Those hazards may come from farm equipment, ponds and irrigation ditches, electrical power for pumps/center pivot operations and electrical fences, traffic, use of agricultural chemicals, weeds such as sand burs and puncture vines that cause mechanical injury, territorial farm dogs, and livestock. Controlling children's activities is important, not only for their safety, but also for the protection of the farmer's livelihood. Open irrigation waters are essential to agriculture and have legal rights of ways that must not be obstructed. Open ditch operations often result in seepage and spills of storm waters in unpredictable locations and times.

(Exhibit continues on next page)

Exhibit 46 (continued)

The BOCC also agrees to:

1. Notify landowners in unincorporated portions of Larimer County about the RTFR Policy by distributing the RTFR Policy and executive summary in all possible manners that the budget allows.

2. Provide landowner education material when a building permit is issued for new construction in unincorporated areas of the county.

3. Initiate amendments to the County subdivision regulations to provide that notification of the RTFR Policy and executive summary shall be made at the time of any subdivision or related land use approval and a note to that effect shall appear on any Plat outside municipalities' growth areas.

4. Encourage title companies and real estate brokers countywide to voluntarily disclose the RTFR Policy and/or executive summary to purchasers of real property in the County. The BOCC will also schedule presentations to the Board of Realtors and other professional organizations to explain the RTFR policy and distribute copies of the policy.

5. Utilize existing, and develop needed, intergovernmental agreements with the cities, towns, and other governmental agencies in the county to assure the effectiveness of this resolution throughout the county.

Source: Larimer County Web site http://www.co.larimer.co.us/policies/right_to_farm_summary.htm

Exhibit 47. Bill of Rights for Animals

Animal rights advocates go beyond animal welfare. This list of animal rights illustrates how they ascribe rights to animals.

---

1. All animals are born with an equal claim on life and the same rights to existence.

2. All animals are entitled to respect. Humanity as an animal species shall not arrogate to itself the right to exterminate or exploit other species. It is humanity's duty to use its knowledge for the welfare of animals. All animals have the right to the attention, care, and protection of humanity.

3. No animals shall be ill-treated or be subject to cruel acts.

4. All wild animals have the right to liberty in their natural environment, whether land, air, or water, and should be allowed to procreate. Deprivation of freedom, even for educational purposes, is an infringement of this right.

5. Animals of species living traditionally in a human environment have the right to live and grow at the rhythm and under the conditions of life and freedom peculiar to their species. Any interference by humanity with this rhythm or these conditions for purposes of gain is an infringement of this right.

6. All companion animals have the right to complete their natural life span. Abandonment of an animal is a cruel and degrading act.

7. Animal experimentation involving physical or psychological suffering is incompatible with the rights of animals, whether it be for scientific, medical, commercial, or any other form of research. Replacement methods must be used and developed.

8. No animal shall be exploited for the amusement of humanity. Exhibitions and spectacles involving animals are incompatible with their dignity.

9. Any act involving the wanton killing of the animals is biocide, that is, a crime against life.

10. Any act involving the mass killing of wild animals is genocide, that is, a crime against the species. Pollution or destruction of the natural environment leads to genocide.

Source: (http://arrs.envirolink.org/bill_of_rights.html). Revised from the original in Charles Magel, *Keyguide to Information Sources Rights* (Jefferson, NC: McFarland, 1989), pp. 233–234.

Exhibit 48. Beef Industry Comments on the Positive Values of Raising Cattle

The beef industry's main counter to people against eating meat is to show how important the beef industry is to our health and well-being. Many pharmaceuticals come from beef by-products, and cattle grazing has been shown to benefit the environment when done properly.

Cattle Enhance the Environment	Graze on about 1.2 billion acres that can't be used for anything else. Cows have a complex four-compartment stomach that enables them to digest types of vegetation that humans can't. About 80–85% of nutrients are from forages and nutrient sources that are not suitable for humans.
Cattle Improve Grass and Reduce Erosion	Aerate the soil with their hooves, press grass seed into soil, provide natural fertilizer.
Cattle Are Recyclers	Eat nonedible by-products of food production such as fruit pits, sugar beet pulp, and potato skins. Cattle consume about 9 million tons annually, which is more than 25 % of all food by-products.
Cattle Are Firefighters	Cattle grazing reduces grass height and fire risk.
Cattle Provide Nutritious Beef	Beef provides complete protein, absorbable iron, zinc, and B vitamins.
Cattle Provide By-Products for Everyday Use:	
Pharmaceuticals	Blood factors for treating hemophilia, chymotrypsin for burns, collagen for plastic surgery, glucagon for hypoglycemia, insulin for diabetes, and B-12.
Travel	Glycerol from fat for antifreeze; binding agents for asphalt, jet, auto, and outboard motor oils and lubricants; glue; and stearic acid in tires to help them hold their shape.
Food	Gelatin, candies, dairy products, Oleo margarine, chewing gum, marshmallows, and jellies.
Household	Candles, ceramics, combs, crayons, deodorants, floor wax, insulation, leather goods, mouthwash, paints, paper, plastic, shaving cream, soaps, textiles, and toothpaste.

Several sources including: American National CattleWomen (n.d.) and http://www.cowtown.org/librref/beefhand/econ2.html

Exhibit 49. Costs of Vandalism on Animal Care or Production Facilities

Some animal rights activists justify vandalism on animal care or production facilities. In some cases the costs of these violent acts can run into the millions. This table shows U.S. Department of Justice estimates for major incidents of vandalism in which direct costs exceeded $10,000.

Date	Enterprise Victimized	Description of Action	Estimate of Direct Cost
4/16/87	University of California-Davis	Arson/Vandalism	$4,500,000
4/20/85	University of California-Riverside	Break-in/Theft	$600,000
12/9/84	City of Hope Research Inst.* and Medical Center, Duarte, CA	Break-in/Theft	$400,000 –$500,000
6/5/88	Sun Valley Meat Packing Company,* San Jose, CA	Arson/Vandalism	$300,000
4/2/89	University of Arizona-Tucson, AZ	Break-in/ Arson/Theft	$250,000
1/29/89	Dixon Livestock Building*, Dixon, CA	Arson/Vandalism	$250,000
11/28/87	V. Melani Poultry*, Santa Clara, CA	Arson/Vandalism	$230,000
11/25/87	Ferrara Meat Company*, San Jose, CA	Arson	$200,000
5/1/86	Simonsen Laboratories*, Gilroy, CA	Vandalism	$165,000
2/28/92	Michigan State University, East Lansing, MI	Break-in/Arson	$125,000
10/24/92	Utah State University, Logan, UT	Break-in/Arson	$110,000
11/10/92	Swanson Meats,* Minneapolis, MN	Arson	+$100,000
12/6/86	SEMA Corporation* and National Institutes of Health, MD	Theft	$100,000
6/10/91	Oregon State University, Corvallis, OR	Break-in/Arson/ Vandalism	$75,000
7/1/89	Texas Tech University, Lubbock, TX	Break-in	$50,000 –$70,000
12/25/83	Harbor-UCLA Medical Center	Break-in/Theft	$58,000
10/26/86	University of Oregon, Eugene, OR	Break-in/Theft	+$50,000
9/1/87	San Jose Valley Veal & Beef Co.*, Santa Clara, CA	Arson	$35,000
5/29/84	University of Pennsylvania, Philadelphia, PA	Break-in/Theft	$20,000
11/24/86	Omega and HMS Turkey Ranches*, Wilton, CA	Theft/Vandalism	$12,000
8/15/88	Loma Linda University, Loma Linda, CA	Break-in/Theft	$10,000

* Indicates a private or otherwise nonacademic enterprise.

Source: Department of Justice (Adapted from Center for Defense of Free Enterprise Web site, http://www.cdfe.org/DOJReport.htm)

Exhibit 50. Land Ownership in the United States

Almost 70 percent of land in the United States is owned by private individuals.

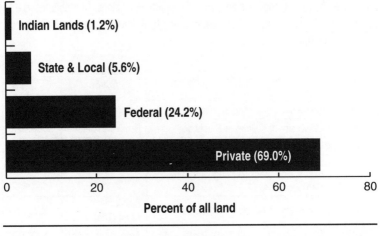

Source: USDA

Exhibit 51. Land Use in 1992

About 30 percent of land use consists of cropland and about 20 percent each consists of forests or rangeland.

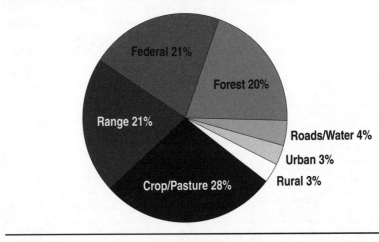

Source: USDA

Exhibit 52. Irrigation Water Use in the West

Water in the West is critical for crop production. On average, agriculture accounts for about 25 percent of national consumptive use (e.g., that which does not end up back in streams). However, in most western states agriculture accounts for well over 90 percent of consumptive use.

State	Irrigation Total (million acre feet)	Irrigation's Share (%) of State Consumptive Use
Arizona	5.9	82
Arkansas	5.9	94
California	31.3	93
Colorado	13.0	94
Florida	4.2	79
Georgia	0.5	54
Idaho	20.9	99
Kansas	4.7	92
Louisiana	0.8	39
Mississippi	2.1	74
Montana	10.1	93
Nebraska	6.8	93
Nevada	3.2	86
New Mexico	3.4	86
Oklahoma	0.7	58
Oregon	7.7	95
Texas	9.5	79
Utah	4.0	87
Washington	6.8	92
Wyoming	8.0	95
All Other States	3.9	25
United States	153.0	81

Source: USDA 1997

Exhibit 53. Fresh Water Use in the Western United States, 1997

Of the freshwater used in western states, about two-thirds comes from surface water and one-third from groundwater. About half is consumptive use and half is return flow. On average, irrigation accounts for 78 percent of water use.

Sources of Water	Uses of Water	Disposition of Water
Surface Water 67% (120 million ac-ft)	Domestic/Commercial 10% (17.5 million ac-ft)	Consumptive Use 46% (81.7 million ac-ft)
Groundwater 33% (58.9 million ac-ft)	Industrial/Mining 3% (5.6 million ac-ft)	Return Flow 54% (97.3 million ac-ft)
	Thermoelectric Power 9% (16.3 million ac-ft)	
	Irrigation/Livestock 78% (140 million ac-ft)	

Source: Western Water Policy Review Advisory Commission Web site 1998

Exhibit 54. An Example of Resolving Agricultural and Other Water-Use Conflicts: The John Day River, Oregon

In 1997, the Bonneville Power Administration will fund $88 million in projects in the Columbia River basin in Washington and Oregon to improve conditions for anadromous fish (migrating upriver from the sea to spawn). The case below illustrates conflicts between agriculture and other water users, and how cooperation can result in positive outcomes for all.

Two farms along the John Day River in Oregon were diverting water to privately owned ditches via three gravel "pushup" dams to irrigate 85 acres of alfalfa. Each diversion had a fish screen to help protect fish. Several times each year, a bulldozer was used to rebuild the diversion dams, which destabilized the channel and added sediment to the river. Ditches and fish screens had to be cleaned regularly as a consequence. Salmon had difficulty passing the diversion dams, and the landowners had difficulty staying within their water rate and duty because of ditch losses and application inefficiency.

A cooperative project between landowners, the Grant County Soil and Water Conservation District, the Oregon Water Resources Department, the USDA Natural Resources Conservation Service, and the Bureau of Reclamation replaced the diversion structures with three diesel pumps and with modern fish screens. The agencies provided about $90,000 in materials and services and landowners contributed about $2,400 and agreed to provide maintenance.

The project produced many benefits, including a 1 ton-per-acre increase in crop yield from more efficient water application, improved salmon passage, reduced soil turbidity, and an overall yearly savings to all of about $16,500.

Source: Western Water Policy Review Advisory Commission Web site 1998

Government and Society

Exhibit 55. Major Policy Acts in the United States Related to Agriculture (1862–1996)

This list includes the major laws that have been passed in this country that affect agriculture.

Government Policy	Year
Homestead Act	1862
Morrill Land-Grant College Act	1862
Organic Act of the Department of Agriculture	1862
Pacific Railway Act	1862
Tariff Act	1864
Desert Land Act	1877
Meat Inspection Act	1884
Hatch Experiment Station Act	1887
Interstate Commerce Act	1887
Morrill Land-Grant College Act	1890
Sherman Antitrust Act	1890
McKinley Tariff Act	1890
Carey Act of 1894	1894
Land Reclamation Act	1902
Federal Food and Drug Act	1906
Federal Meat Inspection Act	1907
Federal Insecticide Act	1910
Clayton Act	1914
Federal Trade Commission Act	1914
Smith-Lever Act	1914
Federal Farm Loan Act	1916
U.S. Grain Standards Act	1916
U.S. Warehouse Act	1916
Smith-Hughes Vocational Education Act	1917
Packers and Stockyards Act	1921
Commodity Exchange Act	1922
Capper-Volstead Act	1922
Agricultural Credit Act	1923
Agricultural Marketing Act	1929

Exhibit 55 (continued)

Government Policy	Year
Hawley-Smoot Tariff Act	1930
Perishable Agricultural Commodities Act	1930
Agricultural Adjustment Act	1933
Emergency Farm Mortgage Act	1933
Farm Credit Act	1933
Executive Order 6084	1933
Executive Order 6340	1933
Federal Surplus Relief Corporation	1933
Tennessee Valley Authority Act	1933
International Wheat Agreement	1933
Civilian Conservation Corps Act	1933
Jones-Connally Act	1934
Jones-Costigan Sugar Act	1934
Bankhead Cotton Control Act	1934
Kerr-Smith Tobacco Control Act	1934
Taylor Grazing Act	1934
Reciprocal Trade Agreements Act	1934
Soil Conservation Act	1935
Warren Potato Act	1935
DeRouen Rice Act	1935
Executive Order 7027	1935
Agricultural Adjustment Act amendments	1935
Hoosac-Mills Decision of Supreme Court	1936
Flood Control Act	1936
Soil Conservation and Domestic Allotment Act	1936
Rural Electrification Administration Act	1936
Robinson-Patman Act	1936
Pope-Jones Water Facilities Act	1937
Sugar Act	1937
International Sugar Agreement	1937
Agricultural Marketing Agreement Act	1937
Bankhead-Jones Farm Tenancy Act	1937
Fair Labor Standards Act	1938
Agricultural Adjustment Act	1938

Exhibit 55 (continued)

Government Policy	Year
Wheeler-Case Act	1939
Food Stamp Program and School Lunch Program	1939
Inter-American Coffee Agreement	1940
Lend-Lease Act	1941
Steagall Amendment (to Lend-Lease Act)	1941
Stabilization Act	1942
Farmers Home Administration Act	1946
Agricultural Research and Marketing Act	1946
National School Lunch Act	1946
Bureau of Land Management Act	1946
General Agreement on Tariffs and Trade Act	1947
Federal Insecticide, Fungicide and Rodenticide Act	1947
Sugar Act	1948
Foreign Assistance Act	1948
Commodity Credit Corporation Charter Act	1948
Agricultural Act	1948
International Wheat Agreement	1949
Agricultural Act	1949
Defense Production Act amendments	1952
Agricultural Act	1954
Agricultural Trade Development and Assistance Act	1954
Amendment to Food and Drug Act	1954
Agricultural Act	1956
Great Plains Conservation Program	1956
Agricultural Act	1958
International Wheat Agreement	1959
Tobacco Price Support Act	1960
Emergency Feed Grain Program	1961
Trade Expansion Act	1962
Food and Agricultural Act	1962
International Wheat Agreement	1962
Feed Grain Act	1963
Agricultural Act	1964
Food Stamp Act	1964

Exhibit 55 (continued)

Government Policy	Year
Meat Import Quota Act	1964
Amendment to Food and Drug Act	1964
Food and Agricultural Act	1965
Water Quality Act	1965
Child Nutrition Act	1966
Food for Peace Act	1966
Agricultural Fair Practices Act	1967
International Grains Agreement	1967
National Environmental Policy Act	1969
Agricultural Act	1970
Environmental Protection Agency	1970
Occupational Safety and Health Act (OSHA)	1970
Rural Environmental Assistance Program	1971
Pesticide Control Act	1972
Rural Development Act	1972
Water Pollution Control Act	1972
Agriculture and Consumer Protection Act	1973
Trade Act	1974
Rice Production Act of 1975	1975
Farmer-to-Consumer Direct Marketing Act	1976
Toxic Substances Control Act	1976
Soil and Water Resources Conservation Act	1977
Food and Agricultural Act	1977
Emergency Assistance Act	1978
Meat Import Act	1979
Federal Crop Insurance Act	1980
Staggers Rail Act	1980
Agriculture and Food Act	1981
Omnibus Budget Reconciliation Act	1982
No-Net-Cost Tobacco Program Act	1982
Extra-Long Staple Cotton Act	1983
Payment-in-Kind Program	1983
Dairy and Tobacco Adjustment Act	1983
Migrant and Seasonal Agricultural Worker Protection Act	1983

Exhibit 55 (continued)

Government Policy	Year
Agricultural Program Adjustment Act	1984
Food Security Act	1985
Balanced Budget and Emergency Deficit Control Act	1985
Farm Credit Restructuring and Regulatory Reform Act	1985
Tax Reform Act	1986
Food Security Improvements Act	1986
Immigration Reform and Control Act	1986
Omnibus Budget Reconciliation Act	1987
Agricultural Credit Act	1987
Disaster Assistance Act	1988
Omnibus Trade and Competitiveness Act	1988
United States-Canada Free Trade Agreement Implementation Act	1988
Disaster Assistance Act	1989
Omnibus Budget Reconciliation Act	1989
Coastal Zone Act	1990
Omnibus Budget Reconciliation Act	1990
Food, Agriculture, Conservation, and Trade Act	1990
Reauthorization amendments	1990
Agricultural Credit Improvement Act	1992
WIC Farmers' Market Nutrition Act	1992
Farm Credit System Agricultural Export & Risk Management Act	1994
Federal Crop Insurance Reform & Department of Agriculture Reorganization Act	1994
Healthy Meals for Healthy Americans Act	1994
Pesticide Safety Training and Labeling Requirements, extension of certain compliance dates	1994
Plant Variety Protection Act amendment	1994
Sheep Promotion, Research, & Information Act	1994
Vegetable Ink Printing Act	1994
Farm Credit System Reform Act	1996
Federal Agriculture Improvement and Reform Act	1996

Sources: Various sources including Hallberg 1992; Lipton and Pollack 1996

Exhibit 56. 1998 USDA Budget by Spending Category

The USDA budget is the second largest for any agency next to the Department of Defense. In 1998, it topped $88 billion. Interestingly, almost half goes to nonagricultural social programs like food stamps. Farm programs, which are being phased out, cost nearly one-quarter of the budget.

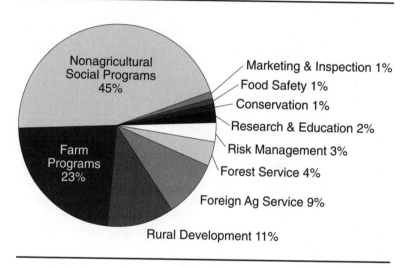

Source: USDA

References

Ahearn, Mary, Jet Yee, Eldon Ball, and Richard Nehring. *Agricultural Productivity in the United States.* Agriculture Information Bulletin No. 740, 21. Washington, DC: Economic Research Service, U.S. Department of Agriculture, 1998.

American National CattleWomen. *Wow That Cow! How Cattle Enrich Our Lives . . . and Enhance the Planet.* Englewood, CO: American National CattleWomen, n.d.

Ames, Bruce. "Science and the Environment: Facts v. Phantoms." *NWI Resource* (Spring 1993): 4. Available at National Wilderness Institute's Web site, http://www.nwi.org/ResourceArticles/Ames.html.

Ames, B., and L. Gold. "Environmental Pollution, Pesticides, and the Prevention of Cancer: Misconceptions." *FASEB Journal* (1997): 11, pp. 1041–1052.

Boehlje, M. "The 'New' Agriculture." *CHOICES* 10(1995): 34–35.

Brown, Lester. *Who Will Feed China? Wake-Up Call for a Small Planet.* The Worldwatch Environmental Alert Series, ed. Linda Starke. New York: W. W. Norton, 1995.

Buzby, J., and T. Roberts. "ERS Updates U.S. Foodborne Disease Costs for Seven Pathogens." *Food Review* (September–December 1996): 20–25.

Center for Defense of Free Enterprise. Web site: http://www.cdfe.org/DOJReport.htm.

Council for Agricultural Science and Technology. *Grazing on Public Lands.* No. 129, Task Force Report. Ames, IA: Center for Agricultural Science and Technology, 1996.

Crutchfield, S., et al. *An Economic Assessment of Food Safety Regulations: The New Approach to Meat and Poultry Inspection.* Agricultural Economics Report No. 755. Washington, DC: U.S. Department of Agriculture, Economic Research Service, 1997.

Daniels, Tom, and Deborah Bowers. *Holding Our Ground.* Washington, DC: Island Press, 1997.

Environmental Working Group. *Pesticide Industry Propaganda: The Real Story.* Washington, DC: Physicians for Social Responsibility and National Campaign for Pesticide Policy Reform, n.d.

Fischer, G., K. Frohberg, M. Parry, and C. Rosenzweig. "Climate Change and World Food Supply, Demand and Trade." *Global Environmental Change,* (1994): 4, 7–23.

Food Marketing Institute. *The Greening of Consumers: A Food Retailer's Guide.* Bellevue, WA: Harman Group, 1997.

Hallberg, M. C. *American Agriculture: Choices and Consequences.* Ames, IA: Iowa State University Press, 1992.

Hayenga, M. "Texas Cattle Feeders v. Oprah Winfrey: The First Major Test of the 'Veggie Libel Law.' " *CHOICES* 13, (Second Quarter, 1998): 13–20

Hoag, D. "Soil Conservation Incentives in the 1985–1996 U.S. Farm-Bills." In *Incentives in Soil Conservation: From Theory to Practice,* edited by David W. Sanders, P. Huszar, S. Smbatpanit, and T. Enters. Enfield, NH: Science Publishers, forthcoming.

Hoag, D., J. Fulton, and E. Hornbrook. Colorado's Farm & Food System: Its Contribution to the State's Economy in 1992. Bulletin 551A. Fort Collins, Colorado: Colorado State University Cooperative Extension, 1995.

Hoag, D. and E. Fathel-Rahman. The Value of Agricultural Research. Experiment Station Report. Fort Collins, Colorado: Colorado State University, forthcoming.

Jaenicke, E. *The Myths and Realities of Pesticide Reduction: A Reader's Guide to Understanding the Full Economic Impacts.* Policy Studies Report No. 8. Greenbelt, MD: Henry A. Wallace Institute for Alternative Agriculture, 1997.

Lipton, Kathryn, and Susan Pollack. "Major Agricultural and Trade Legislation, 1933–96." In *Provisions of the Federal Agricultural Improvement and Reform Act of 1996.* Agriculture Information Bulletin, appendix III, AIB-729 (1996), 128–138. Washington, DC: U.S. Department of Agriculture, Economic Research Service.

Lipton, K., and W. Edmondson. "Linking Agriculture to the Economy." *CHOICES* 8 (Fourth Quarter, 1993): 22–23.

Loomis, John, and Doug White. "Economic Benefits of Rare and Endangered Species: Summary and Meta-Analysis." *Ecological Economics* 18 (1996): 197–206.

Pease, James. *Property Rights, Land Stewardship, and the Takings Issue.* Publication No. EM 8689. Corvallis, OR: Oregon State University Extension Service, 1998.

Rosenberger, R., R. Walsh, and J. McKean. *Benefits of Ranch Open Space to Local Residents.* Report No. XCM-201. Fort Collins, CO: Colorado State University Cooperative Extension, 1996.

Scodari, Paul. *Wetlands Protection: The Role of Economics.* Washington, DC: Environmental Law Institute, 1990.

Smith, Kerry. "Environmental Costing for Agriculture: Will It Be Standard Fare in the Farm Bill of 2000?" *American Journal of Agricultural Economics* 74 (1992): 1076–1088.

Sorensen, A., R. Greene, and K. Russ. *Farming on the Edge*. DeKalb, IL: American Farmland Trust, Center for Agriculture in the Environment, Northern Illinois University, 1997.

Thompson, N., and L. Haskins. *Searching for "Sound Science": A Critique of Three University Studies on the Economic Impacts of Large-Scale Hog Operations*. Walthill, NE: Center for Rural Affairs, 1998.

Tweeten, L. "Anticipating a Tighter Global Food Supply-Demand Balance in the Twenty-First Century." *CHOICES* 13 (Third Quarter, 1998): 8–12.

USDA Economic Research Service. *Agricultural Resources and Environmental Indicators, 1996–97*. Agricultural Handbook No. 712. Washington, DC: U.S. Department of Agriculture, Economic Research Service, 1997.

Western Water Policy Review Advisory Commission. Final Report—Water in the West: *The Challenge for the Next Century*. Denver, CO: 1998. (Available from: www.den.doi.gov/wwprac/reports/final.htm).

World Health Organization. *Bovine Spongiform Encephalopathy (BSE)*. Fact Sheet No. 113 (Revised): 453–463. World Health Organization, November 1996.

Organizations 5

There are literally thousands of organizations that have agricultural connections. Due to limited space, only the groups most active or vocal on agricultural issues have been listed, plus a sampling of the different types of organizations that exist (such as commodity groups). This list was compiled from my own experience, from several thousand names in the National Agricultural Library "GALE Associations" database, and from two published registries: the *Directory of American Agriculture* and the *Directory of American Agribusiness*. Both registries are available from Agricultural Resources and Communications, Inc., 4210 Wam-Teau Drive, Wamego, KS 66547.

Some of these organizations can also be found in Chapter 7 and contacted directly over the Internet. A brief discussion is presented for those organizations that submitted written materials or for which a Web site could be found.

Agricultural Issues Center
University of California, Davis
One Shields Avenue
Davis, CA 95616
Tel: (530) 752-2320
Fax: (530) 752-5451
http://aic/ucdavis.edu

The Agricultural Issues Center (AIC) focuses on international trade, natural resources, advances in agricultural productivity and technology, the role of human resources in agriculture, the impacts of economic policies, and the implications of changing food consumption patterns on agriculture. Research and analysis of public issues are gathered and presented by the AIC to promote interest and education throughout the general public.

Publications: AIC Issues Brief, The UC/AIC Quarterly

American Agriculture Movement
100 Maryland Avenue NE, Suite 500
P.O. Box 69
Washington, DC 20002
Tel: (605) 993-6201

Mission: "The American Agriculture Movement, Inc. has had a policy from the beginning, and will continue into the future, that covers the following five points:
- 100 percent parity for all agriculture products
- All food reserves at 100 percent
- A farmer board at all levels to help make agriculture policy
- Imports would not enter the country below 100 percent parity
- Have a long-range plan for agriculture."
The American Agriculture Movement (AAM) was established in 1977 in response to the government setting prices for agricultural products below the cost of production. A farmer-created, farmer-built organization, the AAM provides a place where farmers can speak for themselves and become involved in government.

Publications: Newsletter

American Crop Protection Association
1156 Fifteenth Street NW, Suite 400
Washington, DC 20005
Tel: (202) 296-1585
http://www.acpa.org

Mission: "The American Crop Protection Association's mission is to further the interest of the general public and ACPA member companies by promoting the environmentally sound use of crop-protection products for the economical production of safe, high-quality, abundant food, fiber, and other crops."

The American Crop Protection Association (ACPA) is a not-for-profit trade organization founded in 1933. It has come to represent the manufacturers, formulators, and distributors of crop products.

Publications: Books and articles dealing with agriculture, the Food Quality Protection Act, food quality and safety, Integrated Pest Management, pesticide testing, and water quality

American Farm Bureau
225 Touhy Avenue
Park Ridge, IL 60068
Tel: (847) 685-8600
Fax: (847) 685-8896
http://www.fb.com/

Mission: "The purpose of Farm Bureau is to make the business of farming more profitable and the community a better place to live. Farm Bureau should provide an organization in which members may secure the benefits of unified efforts in a way which could never be accomplished through individual effort."

Founded in 1919 by a group of farmers representing 30 states, the American Farm Bureau (AFB) is an independent, nongovernmental, voluntary organization of farm and ranch families united for the purpose of analyzing their problems and formulating action plans in order to promote the national well-being of American farmers. Active at local, county, state, and national levels, AFB has become the voice of agricultural producers of all sizes.

Publications: A weekly newsletter, *Farm Bureau News*

American Farmland Trust
1920 N Street NW, Suite 400
Washington, DC 20036
Tel: (202) 659-5170
Fax: (202) 659-8339
http://www.farmland.org

Mission: "To stop the loss of productive farmland and to promote farming practices that lead to a healthy environment."

American Farmland Trust is a nonprofit organization founded in 1980 by a group of farmers and conservationists concerned about the loss of farmland due to development and urban expansion. Since its origination, the group's public policy advocacy has succeeded in having conservation initiatives included in federal farm bills and in helping establish state and local farmland protection programs.

Publications: Farmland Protection Guidebooks and several articles, books, and videos in the following categories: farmland protection techniques, purchase of agricultural conservation easement programs, estate planning, farmland protection research, environmental stewardship, cost of community services, and agricultural fact sheets

American National CattleWomen, Inc.
P.O. Box 3881
Englewood, CO 80155-3881
Tel: (303) 694-0313
Fax: (303) 694-2390
http://www.beef.org/ancw

Mission: "To involve and support its members in promoting beef and the beef cattle industry."
Organized in 1925, American National CattleWomen, Inc. is founded upon volunteer spirit aimed at educating consumers about the wholesomeness of beef products and the beef industry's dedication to environmentally friendly practices.

Publications: Wow That Cow!, Prize Winning National Beef Cook-Off Recipes, a bimonthly newsletter, *The American CattleWoman,* and *Cattle and Beef: The American Industry*

American Society of Animal Science
309 W. Clark Street
Champaign, IL 61820
Tel: (217) 356-3182
Fax: (217) 398-4119
http://www.asas.org

Mission: "To advance animal sciences research and education, through the exchange of scientific and technical information and applications to animal agriculture, public policy and public understanding."

The American Society of Animal Science (ASAS) is a professional organization for animal scientists. As the livestock and meat industries continue to change, the ASAS is designed to help members provide effective leadership through research, extension, teaching, and service.

Publications: Monthly publication of the *Journal of Animal Science*

Animal Industry Foundation
1501 Wilson Boulevard, Suite 1100
Arlington, VA 22209
Tel: (703) 524-0810
Fax: (703) 524-1921
http://www.aif.org/

The Animal Industry Foundation (AIF) was established in 1987 to protect the interests of individuals involved in animal agriculture and to educate the public as to what they contribute to society's quality of life. A source of educational information, AIF is committed to correcting any false or misinterpreted information provided by animal activists.

Publications: "A Teacher Resource Guide to Food Animal Care and Use Issues" (an on-line catalog of booklets and kits to promote agricultural education in the classroom, all levels)

Center for Agricultural and Rural Development
Iowa State University
578 Heady Hall
Ames, IA 50011-1070
Tel: (515) 294-1183
Fax: (515) 294-6336
http://www.ag.iastate.edu/card/

Mission: "An early innovator of complex statistical and mathematical policy modeling systems, our mission now extends to multidisciplinary programs addressing contemporary public policy issues in the domestic and international arenas. CARD conducts internship exchanges with economists, scientists, and practitioners in Eastern and Central Europe, Asia and the Pacific Rim, Africa, and South America."

A public policy research center founded in 1958 at Iowa State University, the Center for Agricultural and Rural Development is a research and teaching unit. Research is conducted in four primary areas: trade and agricultural policy, resource and environmental policy, food and nutrition policy, and rural and economic development policy.

Publications: A news periodical, *CARDreport;* a yearly publications catalog that lists all reports, outlooks, and papers distributed by CARD

Center for Agriculture in the Environment
148 N. 3rd Street
P.O. Box 987
DeKalb, IL 60115
Tel: (815) 753-9347
Fax: (815) 753-9348

The Center for Agriculture in the Environment is a nonprofit research center that conducts public policy research to reduce the loss of productive farmland and to promote farming practices that lead to a healthy environment.

Center for Holistic Management
1010 Tijeras NW
Albuquerque, NM 87102
Tel: (505) 842-5252
Fax: (505) 843-7900
http://www.igc.org/holisticmanagement

Mission: "The Center for Holistic Management is a not-for-profit organization working to restore the vitality of communities and the natural resources on which they depend. This mission is carried out through a range of activities directed at:
- Sharing learning about the physical world and about restorative, creative, and dynamic processes
- Generating the knowledge that real solutions are available to restore the biodiversity upon which all life depends
- Invigorating planning and decisionmaking in communities and family operations
- Enhancing institutional, corporate, and public planning and policy making
- Increasing citizen participation in sound resource management."

Publications: Holistic Management in Practice, a bimonthly journal for holistic management practitioners (until mid-1998, was published under the title *Holistic Management Quarterly*)

Center for Rural Affairs
P.O. Box 406
Walthill, NE 68067-0406
Tel: (402) 846-5428
Fax: (402) 846-5420
http://www.cfra.org

Mission: "The Center for Rural Affairs is committed to building communities that stand for social justice, economic opportunity, and environmental stewardship. We encourage people to accept both personal and social responsibility for creating such communities. We provide opportunities for people to participate in the decisions that shape the quality of their lives and the futures of their communities. The Center engages in research, education, advocacy, and service to further this vision of rural America."

Publications: Free monthly newsletter; 45 titles of books, research reports, and special reports

Committee for Sustainable Agriculture
406 Main Street, Suite 313
Watsonville, CA 95076-4623
Tel: (408) 763-2111
Fax: (408) 763-2112
http://www.csa-efc.org

A leader in sustainable agriculture education for more than 18 years, the Committee for Sustainable Agriculture (CSA) works to bring together growers, researchers, advisers, and industry-related businesses to exchange sustainable farming methods. Strengthening soils, protecting the air and water, encouraging diverse ecosystems, and honoring the rural life are all ideas the CSA would like to work into the present food system.

Environmental Defense Fund
257 Park Avenue South
New York, NY 10010
Tel: (212) 505-2100
http://www.edf.org

The Environmental Defense Fund focuses on reducing emissions of greenhouse gases, eliminating exposure to toxic chemicals and pollution, restoring biodiversity, and safeguarding the world's oceans from pollution and overfishing. Scientists, economists, and attorneys all work together to develop new and practical solutions to some of the most serious environmental problems.

Publications: A newsletter, *EDF Letter; A Nature Journal;* the *Nature Writer;* news releases, reports, and brochures

Environmental Working Group
1718 Connecticut Avenue, Suite 600
Washington, DC 20009
http://www.ewg.org/

The Environmental Working Group (EWG) is a leading provider of information for public-interest groups and concerned citizens who are campaigning to protect the environment. Through reports, articles, technical assistance, and the development of computer databases and Internet resources, EWG's staff of 18 researchers, computer experts, and writers produce hundreds of headline-making reports each year, drawing on original EWG analyses of government and other data.

Publications: Numerous reports on various topics such as air pollution, water quality, pesticide use, and environmental hazards

Farm Foundation
1211 W. 22nd Street, Suite 216
Oak Brook, IL 60523-2197
Tel: (708) 571-9393
Fax: (708) 571-9580
http://www.farmfoundation.org/

Mission: "Farm Foundation's mission is to improve the economic and social well-being of U.S. agriculture and rural people by helping private and public sector decisionmakers identify and understand forces that will shape the future."
Founded in 1933, Farm Foundation was created to promote the understanding of the relationships among natural resources, human capital, technology, institutions, and society.

Publications: A quarterly newsletter, *The Catalyst; Increasing Understanding of Public Problems and Policies,* the proceedings of the annual National Public Policy Education Conference

FarmAid
334 Broadway, Suite 1
Cambridge, MA 02139
Tel: (617) 354-2922
Fax: (617) 354-6992
http://www.justicerecords.com/farmaid/about.html

FarmAid, incorporated in 1985, was established to raise public awareness about the plight of American family farmers and to provide financial assistance to those families whose livelihood depends on agriculture. FarmAid plays a crucial role in educating the American public about the importance of family farmers in preserving our food supply, protecting our natural resources, and creating the economic foundation of rural America.

Publications: FarmAid Update (a quarterly newsletter)

Henry A. Wallace Institute for Alternative Agriculture
9200 Edmonston Road, Suite 117
Greenbelt, MD 20770-1551
Tel: (301) 441-8777
Fax: (301) 220-0164
http://www.hawiaa.org

The Henry A. Wallace Institute for Alternative Agriculture, Inc. is a nonprofit, membership, research, and educational organization. It encourages the adoption of low-cost, resource-friendly, environmentally sound, and economically feasible farming systems. Established in 1983, the Wallace Institute provides leadership, research, and analysis toward advancing national agricultural policies.

Publications: Peer-reviewed, quarterly *American Journal of Alternative Agriculture;* a monthly newsletter, *Alternative Agriculture News;* occasional specialized reports

The Heritage Foundation
214 Massachusetts Avenue NE
Washington, DC 20002-4999
Tel: (202) 546-4400
http://www.heritage.org

Mission: "To formulate and promote conservative public policies based on the principles of free enterprise, limited government, individual freedom, traditional American values, and a strong national defense."

A major research and education institute, the Heritage Foundation began in 1973 as a nonpartisan institution. Its studies are centered upon domestic, economic, foreign, and defense policies. Some typical ideas and values include cutting the size of the federal government, reducing taxes and the power of the IRS, and guaranteeing equality under law for all.

Publications: Magazine, *Policy Review;* articles, books, and reference materials

Institute for Agriculture and Trade Policy
2105 1st Avenue South
Minneapolis, MN 55404-2505
Tel: (612) 870-0453
Fax: (612) 870-4846
http://www.iatp.org

Mission: "The Institute for Agriculture and Trade Policy is a non-profit, independent research and education organization dedicated to fostering economically, socially, and environmentally sustainable communities and regions."

Publications: Bridges, IPR, Global Food Watch, WTO News, NAFTA, Label News, UDHR 50 News, and *Water Currents*

International Food Policy Research Institute
2033 K Street NW
Washington, DC 20006-1002
Fax: (202) 467-4439
http://www.cgiar.org/ifpri

Founded in 1975 to help developing countries establish policies about food and the optimum use of agricultural technologies, the International Food Policy Research Institute aims to combat poverty through the development of better government policies and the use of sustainable economic growth. This task is accomplished by examining such macroeconomic issues as trade, exchange, interest, and wage rates.

Publications: Newsletter, *IFPRI Report;* resource materials; food policy reviews, papers, and reports

Leopold Center for Sustainable Agriculture
Iowa State University
209 Curtiss Hall
Ames, IA 50011-1050
Tel: (515) 294-3711
Fax: (515) 294-9696
http://www.ag.iastate.edu/centers/leopold/Leopold.html

Mission: "Its mandated missions are to identify impacts of agricultural practices, contribute to the development of profitable farming systems that conserve natural resources, and to cooperate with the Iowa State University Extension to inform the public of new findings."

As part of the Iowa Groundwater Protection Act of 1987, the Iowa Legislature established the Leopold Center at Iowa State University.

National Cattlemen's Beef Association
5420 South Quebec
Greenwood Village
P.O. Box 3469
Englewood, CO 80155-3469
Tel: (303) 694-0305
http://www.beef.org/

Vision: "A dynamic and profitable beef industry, which concentrates resources around a unified plan, consistently meets consumers needs, and increases demand."

The National Cattlemen's Beef Association was originally established in 1898 to represent the needs of America's beef producers. Today it represents more than 1 million cattle farmers and ranchers in the United States.

Publications: Weekly newsletter, *Beef Business Bulletin; IRM News;* newsletter, *Meat Marketing Quarterly;* newsletter, *Producer Information News;* newsletter, *Research/Meat Science Update; The Beef Brief*

National Corn Growers Association
1000 Executive Parkway, Suite 105
St. Louis, MO 63141-6397
Tel: (314) 275-9915
Fax: (314) 275-7061
http://www.ncga.com

The ultimate goal of the National Corn Growers Association (NCGA) is to increase the value of the nation's number-one crop from $25 billion to $40 billion (farm gate value) by the year 2002. NCGA serves the educational, political, production, and market-development interests of 30,000 grower members and 48 state-affiliated organizations across the United States. NCGA also conducts outreach efforts to other farm organizations, industry leaders, and consumers.

Publications: World of Corn, an annual report of the U.S. corn industry; *Corn Grower Newsletter*, a quarterly newsletter to members and industry partners; *Corn Grower Insert*, a bimonthly insert in *Top Producer* magazine; and many others

National Council of Farmer Cooperatives
50 F Street NW, Suite 900
Washington, DC 20001
Tel: (202) 626-8700
http://www.ncfc.org/

Mission: "To protect the public policy environment in which farmer-owned cooperative businesses operate, promote their economic well-being, and provide leadership in cooperative education."

Founded in 1929, the National Council of Farmer Cooperatives remains the only organization serving exclusively as the national representative and advocate for America's farmer-owned cooperative businesses.

Publications: A bimonthly newsletter, *Cooperator Newsletter*

National Farmers Organization
2505 Elwood Drive
Ames, IA 50010-2000
Tel: (515) 292-2000
Fax: (515) 292-7106
http://www.nfo.org

National Farmers Organization (NFO) is a producer-owned organization that trades agricultural commodities on behalf of its members. Serving as an agent in the marketplace, the not-for-profit NFO operates in 37 states.

Publications: A bimonthly newsletter, *NFO Reporter*

National Farmers Union
10065 E. Harvard Avenue
Denver, CO 80231
Tel: (303) 337-5500
Fax: (303) 368-1390
http://www.nfu.org

Mission: "To protect and enhance the economic interests and quality of life of farmers and ranchers and rural communities."

Publications: Monthly bulletin, the *NFU News*

National Future Farmers of America Organization
6060 FFA Drive
P.O. Box 68960
Indianapolis, IN 46268-0999
Tel: (317) 802-6060
Fax: (317) 802-6061
http://www.ffa.org

Mission: "FFA makes a positive difference in the lives of students by developing their potential for premier leadership, personal growth, and career success through agricultural education."

Future Farmers of Americ (FFA) a is a national organization of more than 450,000 members preparing for leadership and careers in the science, business, and technology of agriculture. The organization has 7,263 local chapters throughout the United States, Puerto Rico, Guam, and the Virgin Islands. Local, state, and national activities and award programs provide opportunities for students to apply knowledge and skills learned in the classroom.

Publications: A bimonthly magazine, *New Horizons;* a monthly magazine for FFA advisers, *FFA Advisors Making a Difference*

National Pork Producers Council
P.O. Box 10383
Des Moines, IA 50306
Tel: (515) 223-2600
Fax: (515) 223-2646
http://www.nppc.org

Mission: "To enhance opportunities for the success of U.S. pork producers and other industry stakeholders by establishing the U.S. pork industry as a consistent and responsible supplier of high-quality pork to the domestic and world market, making U.S. pork the consumer's meat of choice."

Addressing issues from production to consumer demand, the National Pork Producers Council serves as the unified voice for pork producers. Affiliated associations exist in 44 states.

Publications: A biweekly newsletter, *Pork Leader;* quarterly magazine, *Pork Report;* quarterly newsletter, *Tech Talk,* for those involved with the technical side of the industry; yearly *Pork Issues Handbook;* news releases and various reports

Natural Resources Defense Council
1350 New York Avenue NW, Suite 300
Washington, DC 20005
Tel: (202) 783-7800
http://mail.igc.apc.org/nrdc

Mission: "The Natural Resources Defense Council's purpose is to safeguard the Earth: its people, its plants and animals, and the natural systems on which all life depends."
    Dedicated to establishing sustainability and good stewardship of the earth, the Natural Resources Defense Council works to advance the long-term welfare of nature for present and future generations.

Publications: Quarterly magazine, *The Amicus Journal;* a variety of books dealing with all aspects of the world's natural resources

The Nature Conservancy International Headquarters
1815 North Lynn Street
Arlington, VA 22209
Tel: (703) 841-5300
http://www.tnc.org

Mission: "To preserve plants, animals, and natural communities that represent the diversity of life on Earth by protecting the lands and waters they need to survive."
    The Nature Conservancy operates the largest private system of nature sanctuaries in the world—more than 1,500 preserves in the United States alone—that range in size from inches to thousands of acres. All land purchased by the Nature Conservancy is used to safeguard endangered species of plants and animals.

Publications: A bimonthly magazine, *Nature Conservancy*

Poultry Science Association
309 W. Clark Street
Champaign, IL 61820
Tel: (217) 356-3182
Fax: (217) 398-4119
http://www.psa.uiuc.edu/

The Poultry Science Association is a professional organization consisting of educators, scientists, extension specialists, administrators, and producers who are committed to advancing the poultry industry.

Publications: Monthly journal, *Poultry Science;* a quarterly newsletter, *PSA Newsletter*

Rodale Institute
611 Siegfriedale Road
Kutztown, PA 19530-9320
Tel: (610) 683-1487
Fax: (610) 683-9175

The Rodale Institute is a nonprofit charity dedicated to working internationally to achieve a regenerative food system that renews environmental and human health. Using education, communication, and research, the institute shares information locally and abroad with farmers, consumers, food industry leaders, policy makers, and children—the most powerful potential agents for change.

Publications: Catalog of publications available by contacting the Rodale Institute

Sierra Club
85 Second Street, Second Floor
San Francisco, CA 94105-3441
Tel: (415) 977-5500
http://www.sierraclub.org/

Mission: "To explore, enjoy, and protect the wild places of the Earth; to practice and promote the responsible use of the Earth's ecosystems and resources; to educate and enlist humanity to protect and restore the quality of the natural and human environment; and to use all lawful means to carry out these objectives."

The Sierra Club is very involved in agricultural issues due to their impact on wildlife. Representatives of the organization actively lobby state and federal legislators and work on many projects in cooperation or confrontation with local farmers and ranchers.

Publications: A bimonthly magazine, *Sierra;* a newsletter (ten issues per year), *The Planet*

Society for Range Management
1839 York Street
Denver, CO 80206
Tel: (303) 355-7070
Fax: (303) 355-5059
http://srm.org

Mission: "The mission of the Society for Range Management is to promote and enhance the stewardship of rangelands to meet human needs based on science and sound policy."

Established in 1948, the Society for Range Management is a scientific society and conservation organization dedicated to studying, conserving, and sustaining the resources of rangelands.

Publications: Journal of Range Management; Rangeland; both are published six times per year

Soil and Water Conservation Society
7515 NE Ankeny Road
Ankeny, IA 50021
Tel: (515) 289-2331
Fax: (515) 289-1227
http://www.swcs.org/

Mission: "The Soil and Water Conservation Society fosters the science and the art of soil, water, and related natural resource management to achieve sustainability. We promote and practice an ethic recognizing the interdependence of people and the environment."

Publications: Quarterly journal, *Journal of Soil and Water Conservation;* conservationists newsletter, *Conservogram*

Sustainable Agriculture Coalition
110 Maryland Avenue NE
Washington, DC 20002
Tel: (202) 547-5754
Fax: (202) 547-1837

The Sustainable Agriculture Coalition is composed of 12 nonprofit family farm, food, and environmental groups. Members work together to promote changes in federal policy to support sustainable agriculture in the United States.

Publications: Reports and position papers; recommended reading: *Sustaining Land, People, Animals and Communities: Policy Principles for Sustainable Livestock Development*

Winrock International Institute for Agricultural Development
38 Winrock Drive
Morrilton, AK 72110-9370
Tel: (501) 727-5435
http://www.winrock.org/

The Winrock International Institute for Agricultural Development is a private, nonprofit organization. Dedicated to building a better world through increased agricultural productivity and rural employment, the Winrock Institute also strives to protect the environment.

Publications: A quarterly newsletter, *Seeds*

World Resources Institute
1709 New York Avenue NW
Washington, DC 20006
Tel: (202) 638-6300
Fax: (202) 638-0036
http://www.wri.org/wri/

Mission: "[World Resources Institute's] mission is to move human society to live in ways that protect the Earth's environment and its capacity to provide for the needs and aspirations of current and future generations."

Publications: Several booklets, papers, and resource packets on the global environment intended for policymakers, business leaders, educators, and other professionals or citizen groups

Related Print Resources

6

Given the wide scope and availability of literature on agriculture, only a few of the most relevant publications are listed here. More information can be found in several literature-searching services available for agriculture. For example, many libraries subscribe to the AGRICOLA[1] (AGRICultural OnLine Access) database. It can also be accessed directly on the Internet through the National Agricultural Library at http://www. nal.usda.gov/. In general, the Internet provides another good source for printed materials. Many of the agencies, institutes, and organizations publish on-line materials related to their particular interests. A comprehensive list of relevant Internet sites can be found in Chapter 7. Finally, a commercial site with an

---

[1] Subject coverage: agriculture (general); agriculture products; animal sciences; biotechnology; botany; chemistry; conservation; cytology; economics, agricultural; education, agricultural; energy, agricultural; engineering, agricultural; entomology; farm management; feed science; fertilizers; fibers and textiles; food and nutrition; forestry; history, agricultural; horticulture; human ecology; human nutrition; hydrology; hydroponics; information systems for agriculture; microbiology; natural history; natural resources; pesticides; physiology; plant sciences; pollution; public health; rural sociology; soil sciences; veterinary medicine; water quality; weather and climate; wildlife; zoology.

extensive library of books for sale on the Internet is Amazon: http:/ /www.amazon.com.

American Farm Bureau Federation. **Farm Facts.** Park Ridge, IL: American Farm Bureau Federation Public Relations Division, 1998. 26 pp.

This is a nice color publication filled with well-presented farm facts. It includes sections on consumers, farmers, economics of agriculture, trade, production, and history. It can be purchased from the American Farm Bureau Federation for a nominal charge or it can be accessed directly on the Web at http://www.fb.com/today/ farmfacts.

Avery, Dennis. **Saving the Planet with Pesticides and Plastic.** Indianapolis, IN: Hudson Institute, 1995. 432 pp.

Avery turns most of the arguments used by interest groups like environmentalists and technophobes on their heads by arguing that technology is not only good, it provides solutions to the problems environmentalists care about. Avery challenges many environmental facts, then repackages them to tell a very different story. His basic premise is that technology is essential to feed a growing world because it enables people to grow more food on less land. Growing food on less land requires chemicals, but chemicals, he maintains, are far less destructive to the environment than is cultivation. A concentrated farming system provides more natural habitat, reduces soil erosion that washes silt into streams, leaves more forests to enjoy, and conserves freshwater. A world without the technological advances we've seen in the last 30 years would be ravaging the countryside to feed itself.

Chapter titles include: "Preventing Cancer with Pesticides," "The Empty Threat of DDT," and "Organic Farming Can't Save the Environment." For a counterpoint, read Hewitt and Smith's *Intensive Agriculture and Environmental Quality: Examining the Newest Agricultural Myth,* published by the Henry A. Wallace Institute for Alternative Agriculture in Greenbelt, Maryland (1995).

Ball, C. **Building the Beef Industry—A Century of Commitment— 1898–1998.** Saratoga, WY: Saratoga Publishing Group, 1997. 300 pp.

This book is published in association with the National Cattlemen's Foundation to honor the association's 100 years of history. National Cattlemen's led the American cattle industry for a century and continues to thrive. This book describes the people, places, politics, and policies that built an American tradition and lifestyle in the cattle industry. There are 12 chapters, 300 color pages, 400 illustrations, historical photographs, and artwork. Many contemporary topics are discussed, including the future of the beef industry.

Barlett, Peggy F. **American Dreams, Rural Realities: Family Farms in Crisis.** Chapel Hill, NC: University of North Carolina Press, 1993. 305 pp.

Using Dodge County, Georgia, as a case study, the author explores the impact and implications of the American farm crisis on the family farm. Her study provides background information on the conditions that lead to the farm income crisis in the mid-1980s, describes the agricultural environment of the 1980s, and looks for farm-management strategies or qualities that helped ensure the financial success of family farms. Interestingly, Barlett found that the riskier management styles often lead to failure of the family farm, that bigger farms are not necessarily better, and that farming is increasingly a closed career. She spends an entire chapter looking at the concerns of farm women and their connection, or lack thereof, to the land. This is a very good book for those interested in exploring how farm values and family roles evolved in response to changes in the world outside agriculture.

Brown, Lester. **Who Will Feed China? Wake-Up Call for a Small Planet.** Worldwatch Environmental Alert Series, ed. Linda Starke. New York: W. W. Norton, 1995. 163 pp.

Brown has been called the leading modern-day Malthusian. In this book he sounds the alarm about the developing billion-person food-eating machine in China. The impacts on world food markets and the environment, he contends, could be devastating. Brown asserts that the world is shifting from an economic era to an environmental era. Population growth in China will increase environmental degradation of land and water, threatening China's ability to feed its people. Unchecked growth will stress the environment at a time when we cannot afford to degrade our resources any further.

Browne, William, Jerry Skees, Louis Swanson, Paul Thompson, and Laurian Unnevehr. **Sacred Cows and Hot Potatoes: Agrarian Myths in Agricultural Policy.** Boulder, CO: Westview Press, 1992. 150 pp.

This book won the award for best policy publication by the American Agricultural Economics Association. The authors work in the areas of political science, economics, and agriculture, and they have vast collective experience. The book is critical of traditional farm beliefs and government supports. Chapter titles reveal a lot about the book. They include, "Never Assume That Agrarian Values Are Simple," "Never Confuse Farming with Rural America," "Never Equate Good Farming with a Healthy Environment," and "Never Assume That a Government Program Will Do What It Says."

Castle, Emery, ed. **The Changing American Countryside: Rural People and Places.** St. Lawrence, KS: University Press of Kansas, 1995. 563 pp.

In an attempt to improve the understanding of rural life and rural conditions, this book presents discussions of numerous facets of rural people and places in America. The audience to which it is addressed includes people in the position to influence public policy, professors, students, and anyone with interest in rural America.

The book, a result of the work of the National Rural Studies Committee, is a compilation of work by many authors chosen to reflect the viewpoints of numerous academic disciplines in institutions of higher learning. The eight sections include an introduction; reading the land; literature and the countryside; change in the countryside; money, jobs, and space; distress and poverty; regional and ethnic diversity; and group decisionmaking in the countryside. The book makes excellent reading and includes more than 100 figures, tables, and photographs.

Cheeke, P. **Contemporary Issues in Animal Agriculture.** 2d ed. Danville, IL: Interstate Publishers, 1998. 256 pp.

This is a very detailed and technical description of issues related to livestock management, including grazing, biotechnology, food safety, and sustainability.

Diamond, Henry, and Patrick Noonan. **Land Use in America.** Washington, DC: Island Press, 1996. 351 pp.

This book addresses "what has happened to land use since 1973," based on a book from that year titled *The Use of Land: A Citizens' Policy Guide to Urban Growth* by William K. Reilly. The authors were curious about why, since land is such a central resource, attention to land use hasn't moved forward in step with other environmental agendas. This book reports the current state of private land use in America. According to the authors, their purpose is to help communities throughout the country face the challenge of accommodating growth in better, more environmentally sound, and more fiscally responsible ways. The book also evaluates the progress in land use over the last 25 years.

Drabenstott, M., and A. Barkema. **"A New Vision for Agricultural Policy."** *Federal Reserve Bank of Kansas City Economic Review* (1995): 63–78.

Drabenstott and Barkema outline a new vision for agricultural policy in the United States. They suggest that past policy goals and programs are not relevant for the current agricultural industry. Yesterday's small farms have evolved into today's global supermarket. The rural economy is now more diversified and less dependent on farming. The future of agricultural policy lies in the pursuit of four key goals: enhancing international competitiveness, improving the nation's diet, conserving the nation's natural resources, and increasing economic opportunity in rural America.

Finsen, L., and S. Finsen. **The Animal Rights Movement in America: From Compassion to Respect.** New York: Twayne Publishers, 1994. 309 pp.

The authors detail the historical and philosophical rise of the modern American animal rights movement from the late 1800s to the mid-1990s, including the emergence of animal rights as distinct from animal welfare. The book has chapters on organizations, tactics, and politics; issues and campaigns of the 1980s; industry opposition to the rights movement; philosophies of animal rights; environmentalism, ecofeminism, and animal liberation; and projections for the future.

Fitchen, Janet M. **Endangered Spaces, Enduring Places.** Boulder, CO: Westview Press, 1991. 314 pp.

Fitchen examines how urbanization and abandonment threaten rural communities. Through a case study in New York State, she examines how rural places and the social matrix of rural life might be transformed or redefined as communities adapt in the future. Specific topics include: the farm crisis and its challenge to rural community life; a shifting nonfarm economy; changing circumstances; changing rural populations; worsening rural poverty; increasing demands on community services; challenges to local government; new uses for rural land; and rural identity and survival.

Food Marketing Institute, Research Department. **The Greening of Consumers: A Food Retailer's Guide.** Washington, DC: Food Marketing Institute, 1997. 34 pp.

In this report, findings are presented from market research (self-administered surveys) conducted by the Harman Group among a nationally representative sample of U.S. consumers. Depending on their level of interest in purchasing environmentally friendly products, consumers are divided into six distinct segments: true naturals, new green mainstream, young recyclers, affluent healers, overwhelmed, and unconcerned. Information is provided on each segment's attitudes, demographics, and shopping behaviors. From this, specific suggestions and strategies are provided to help retailers market to the 52 percent of Americans who form the potential market for green products.

Gordon, Douglass K., ed. **Agricultural Sustainability in a Changing World Order.** Boulder, CO: Westview Press, 1984. 282 pp.

This book explores the different meanings of sustainability. The standard definition of sustainability is food self-sufficiency. In this view, agriculture is an instrument for feeding the world, and technology is substituted for natural resources (for example, topsoil and water quality are sacrificed for technologies such as fertilizer and water treatment). The authors explore a variety of viewpoints about sustainability. Lester Brown and his followers, for example, define sustainability as an agricultural system that "... honors the long-term biophysical constraints of nature." Alternative Agriculture, another viewpoint, is concerned with the effects of technological change on the social systems found in rural areas. This school of thinking is interested in preserving vital rural communities, and it encourages the values of "stewardship, self-reliance, humility, and holism."

Hanson, Victor Davis. **Field without Dreams—Defending the Agrarian Idea.** New York: Simon & Schuster, Free Press Paperbacks, 1996. 289 pp.

This book, written from the perspective of a Greek scholar and farmer, shares the experiences of farming in the San Joaquin Valley in California during the 1980s and early 1990s. Hanson writes about the disappearance of the family farm and the agrarian ideal. The family farm is not romanticized; rather, he gives a realistic view of the future of farming and looks at those farmers who continue to farm knowing that, in his view, they have no future.

Knutson, Ronald, J. B. Penn, and Barry Flinchbaugh. **Agricultural and Food Policy.** 4th ed. Upper Saddle River, NJ: Prentice-Hall, 1998. 521 pp.

Although this is a textbook for college students, it is still useful to a broader audience. The authors provide a thorough discussion of policies in American agriculture in four parts: process; international trade and macroeconomic policy; domestic farm and resource policy; and consumers, rural development, and agribusiness.

Loomis, John. **Integrated Public Lands Management: Principles and Applications to National Forests, Parks, Wildlife Refuges, and BLM Lands.** New York: Columbia University Press, 1993. 472 pp.

Loomis integrates various economic concepts for a comprehensive review of the policies of federal agencies responsible for resource planning. This well-written book covers history and the use of public lands. Loomis convincingly uses numerous examples to demonstrate how conflicts over multiple use can be addressed.

Luttrell, C. **The High Cost of Farm Welfare.** Washington, DC: CATO Institute, 1989. 149 pp.

This book describes how the government came to be so involved in the farm sector during this century. Major farm programs are reviewed. The theme of the book is that farm programs have outlived their usefulness, if indeed there ever was any value to them. Luttrell argues that farm programs have done more harm than good by exacerbating America's chronic overproduction problems. Farmers who receive support dollars are not downtrodden, poor individuals. Rather, many are affluent, Luttrell contends.

Opie, John. **The Law of the Land: Two Hundred Years of American Farmland Policy.** Lincoln, NE: University of Nebraska Press, 1994. 231 pp.

Opie strongly challenges the notion that private property rights and proprietary independence play an important role in the growth and prosperity of American agriculture. He examines how policies, beginning in 1785, might have played a role in current environmental problems linked to agriculture. For example, he emphasizes how government policies that fostered a belief in individual self-sufficiency also diminished broader social considerations such as soil conservation and preservation of clean water. This book provides a good example of the philosophical camp that believes unbridled capitalism is not sustainable. Opie is thoughtful about his points but does not present a balanced representation of counterarguments.

Rifkin, Jeremy. **Beyond Beef: The Rise and Fall of the Cattle Culture.** New York: Plume, 1993. 353 pp.

Beyond Beef is one of the key books that shaped the movement to challenge traditional notions about the consumption of animals. Rifkin asserts that beef consumption has led to increased hunger, disease, and environmental devastation. His book includes anthropology, history, sociology, economics, and ecology to demonstrate how the "cattle culture" has changed our world. Rifkin has become a key figure in the fight against technology in agriculture and in the movement to reduce, if not eliminate, beef consumption.

Rogers, Earl, and Susan H. Rogers. **The American Farm Crisis—An Annotated Bibliography.** New York: Garland Publishing, 1989. 149 pp.

This book contains a detailed bibliography of the farm crisis of the 1980s and its historical background. It focuses on the causes and magnitude plus economic, sociological, and political solutions. Its largest sections contain general information and economic and sociological analysis of the farm crisis of the 1980s. Sources include articles, books, congressional hearings, other government documents, land-grant university bulletins, and theses.

Sanderson, F. H., ed. **Agricultural Protectionism in the Industrialized World.** Washington, DC: Resources for the Future, 1990. 488 pp.

Written during the late 1980s when much of the developed world was reviewing its domestic agricultural policies, this book chronicles the levels and costs of farm programs in six industrialized nations, including the United States and the European Community.

There is a close relationship between international trade policies for agricultural products and the domestic agricultural policies of the trade partners. Also, agricultural protection seems to be a by-product of economic development, which was becoming an excessive tax burden during the early 1980s. The authors conclude that there is a need to restructure agricultural policy. The chapter (by Bruce Gardner) on the United States outlines commodity programs, lists participation rates in certain programs, and provides market analysis for heavily subsidized commodities, like sugar. The second part of the book deals with lessons from domestic agricultural and trade policies and calculates the welfare impact of freeing up agricultural trade.

Sargent, Frederic, Paul Lusk, Jose A. Rivera, and Maria Varela. **Rural Environmental Planning for Sustainable Communities.** Washington, DC: Island Press, 1991. 254 pp.

This book was written as a guide for planners, rural citizens, public officials, and others looking for information about how to manage local resources and preserve or improve a community's quality of life. Rural Environmental Planning (REP) is a proposed method used by citizens in smaller towns and rural areas to plan for their own future. The strength of REP is derived from the direct participation of those people affected by the plan. Compared with conventional planning, which sees growth as inevitable and increasing the tax base as the primary goal, REP focuses on public goals. The book is divided into three sections: a historical context for planning as well as an overview of REP and how to get started; a more detailed look at the components of REP; and the process of rural development.

Singer, Peter. **Animal Liberation.** New York: Avon Books, 1991. 320 pp.

This is a seminal work for the animal rights movement. It is the first book to draw a connection between speciesism, sexism, and racism, and one of the first books to make popular the concept of "factory farming." Singer is thoughtful and articulate. This is an excellent book to get a more balanced view about why animal rights advocates think what they do. Singer has gone on to become a leader in the animal rights movement and in philosophy on life and death (see biography in Chapter 3).

U.S. Department of Agriculture, Economic Research Service, Market and Trade Economics Division. **International Agricultural Baseline Projections to 2007.** Agricultural Economic Report No. 767. Report coordinators: Rip Landes, Paul Westcott, and John Wainio. Washington, DC: U.S. Department of Agriculture, 1997. 180 pp.

This report provides baseline projections for international supply, demand, and trade for major agricultural commodities to 2007. It is a companion report to *Agricultural Baseline Projections to 2007* (WAOB-98-1), providing the foreign country detail supporting those projections. Projections of strong global economic growth, particularly in developing countries, combined with more open foreign markets and the emergence of China as a major bulk commodity importer support strong projected gains in U.S. farm exports. The value of total U.S. agricultural exports is projected to rise from a record $57.3 billion in FY 1997 to nearly $85 billion in 2007. The projections are a conditional scenario, assuming the continuation of 1996 U.S. farm legislation through 2007, no shocks, average weather, and specific macroeconomic and foreign country policy assumptions. The projections were completed based on information available as of December 1997, and they reflect a composite of model results and analyst judgment.

U.S. General Accounting Office. **Animal Agriculture: Information on Waste Management and Water Quality Issues.** Report GAO/RCED-95-200BR. Washington, DC: U.S. General Accounting Office, 1995. 91 pp.

Describes and provides numerous graphs and tables summarizing (1) water quality concerns arising from animal agriculture sources of nonpoint pollution—pollution not traceable to a specific point of origin; (2) consolidation trends and geographic shifts in animal agriculture; (3) animal agriculture production covered by point source permits; (4) commonly used animal waste management practices and their costs; and (5) USDA cost-share assistance for animal waste management.

Selected Publications from the Council on Agriculture, Science, and Technology (CAST)

Following is a list and partial description of some of the print publications offered by CAST. This organization picks leading specialists to write about current issues in agriculture and is therefore a very good source of information. A complete list of publications available and a full description of each can be found at CAST's Web site, http://www.cast-science.org.

Challenges Confronting Agricultural Research at Land Grant Universities.
Chair: James R. Fischer, South Carolina Agricultural Experiment Station, Clemson University, Clemson. IP5, November 1994. 12 pp.

Agricultural, corporate, scientific, political, environmental, and social communities are asking the agricultural research system to identify and pursue a broadened range of research priorities. This publication highlights where priorities lie for land-grant universities and other agricultural researchers.

Competitiveness of U.S. Agriculture and the Balance of Payments.
Chair: Maury E. Bredahl, Department of Agricultural Economics, University of Missouri-Columbia. R125, October 1995. 34 pp.

U.S. agricultural producers and food processors will need to focus on adding value to agricultural products in a way that meets the needs and desires of an increasingly diverse group of consumers around the world. If it does not focus on consumer need, the U.S. will be relegated to supplying homogeneous commodities that are transformed into value-added food products in foreign countries.

The Conservation Reserve: A Survey of Research and Interest Groups. Hughes, Jennie, Dana Hoag, and Terry Nipp SP19, July 1995. 44 pp.

This summary of research literature on the Conservation Reserve Program includes a detailed survey of 18 interest groups and hundreds of publications from a variety of disciplines.

Contribution of Animal Products to Healthful Diets.
Chair: Donald C. Beitz, Iowa State University, Ames. R131, October 1997. 56 pp.

Foods derived from animals contribute significantly to total nutrients in the U.S. food supply. Moreover, the availability to humans of the nutrients in animal products is high.

Diversifying U.S. Crop Production.
Chair: Jules Janick, Purdue University, West Lafayette, Indiana. IP6, February 1996. 12 pp.

For more than a century, crop price instability has dogged U.S. farmers. And in the past 60 years—despite federal subsidy and acreage reduction programs meant to stabilize farm income—farm numbers, farm populations, and rural prosperity have declined ominously. The development of new crops could help solve all these problems.

Ecological Impacts of Federal Conservation and Cropland Reduction Programs.
Chair: John R. Abernathy, Texas A&M Research and Extension Center, Lubbock. R117, September 1990. 28 pp.

Addresses the ecological implications of several programs established in the 1985 Food Security Act, including the Conservation Reserve Program, Sodbuster, Swampbuster, Conservation Compliance, and Acreage Reduction Program. The authors include persons with expertise in many disciplines.

Examination of Dietary Recommendations for Salt-Cured, Smoked, and Nitrite-Preserved Foods.
Chair: Michael W. Pariza, Food Research Institute, University of Wisconsin-Madison. IP8, November 1997. 8 pp.

The scientific evidence does not support restrictions in the consumption of salted, smoked, or nitrite-preserved foods by the U.S. population.

Food Fats and Health.
Chair: Donald C. Beitz, Iowa State University. R118, December 1991. 96 pp.

This report supports dietary recommendations to decrease food fat consumption from the present national average of 37 percent to less than 30 percent of the total caloric intake. The agricultural and food industries are responding by redesigning fresh and processed foods so that consumers can more readily meet these recommendations.

Food Safety: The Interpretation of Risk.
Author: F. J. Francis, University of Massachusetts at Amherst. CC1992-1, April 1992. 23 pp.

This report states that the amazing advances in analytical methods have made the Delaney Clause hopelessly obsolete and it should be repealed. The Delaney Clause, which states that no amount of cancer-causing substances can be added to food, should be replaced with a "de minimis" concept.

Foodborne Pathogens: Risks and Consequences.
Cochairs: Peggy M. Foegeding, Department of Food Science, North Carolina State University, Raleigh, and Tanya Roberts, Economic Research Service, U.S. Department of Agriculture. R122, September 1994. 87 pp.

The authors conclude that better data on microbial risks are needed to make the U.S. food supply safer.

Future of Irrigated Agriculture.
Chair: Henry J. Vaux, Division of Agriculture and Natural Resources, University of California. R127, August 1996. 76 pp.

Farmers irrigating in the western United States face a host of changing circumstances that will require innovations and new adaptations to ensure continued prosperity.

Grazing on Public Lands.
Chair: William A. Laycock, University of Wyoming, Laramie. R129, December 1996. 70 pp.

Approximately 262 million acres of public land in the western United States are grazed by domestic livestock. This report discusses and provides scientific information concerning livestock grazing on public lands in the West.

Herbicide-Resistant Crops.
Authors: Stephen O. Duke, A. Lawrence Christy, F. Dana Hess, and Jodie S. Holt. CC1991-1, May 1991. 24 pp.

This report indicates that biotechnology-induced herbicide resistance in crops will allow use of herbicides that are toxicologically and environmentally less suspect than those herbicides now used in some crops.

How Much Land Can Ten Billion People Spare for Nature?
Author: Paul E. Waggoner, Connecticut Agricultural Experiment Station, New Haven. (John McCarthy has made the full report available on-line at http://www-formal.stanford.edu/jmc/nature/nature.html.) R121, February 1994. 64 pp.

Advances in farming technology combined with changing values and diets could ensure that the world's population will use existing cropland more economically and thus save more land for natural or wilderness use in the next 50 years.

Integrated Animal Waste Management.
Cochairs: Alan L. Sutton, Purdue University, West Lafayette, Indiana, and James F. Power, USDA, Agricultural Research Service, Lincoln, Nebraska. R128, November 1996. 87 pp.

A broad spectrum of integrated manure-management systems are available to collect, transfer, store, treat, and efficiently utilize a great variety of sources and nutrient qualities of animal manures.

Labeling of Food-Plant Biotechnology Products.
Chair: Susan F. Barefoot, Department of Food Science, Clemson University, Clemson, South Carolina. IP4, July 1994. 8 pp.

This report reviews scientific evidence in response to proposed U.S. Food and Drug Administration policy for labeling of foods from new plant varieties.

Mycotoxins: Economic and Health Risks.
Chairs: John L. Richard, USDA, ARS, and Richard J. Cole, USDA, ARS. R116, December 1989. 99 pp.

This report stresses the importance of the economic and health risks of naturally occurring fungal toxins known as mycotoxins. These diverse toxins potentially occur in foods and feeds and can cause a wide range of injury when consumed by humans and animals. The report covers animal health, human health, occurrence, economic impacts, control and management, and research needs.

Naturally Occurring Antimicrobials in Food.
Chair: John N. Sofos, Colorado State University, Fort Collins. R132, April 1998. 103 pp.

Many biologically derived substances exhibit antimicrobial properties in the foods in which they normally are found or may be developed for commercial use as additives to other foods requiring preservation.

Pesticides: Minor Uses/Major Issues.
Chair: Kenneth P. Dorschner, retired, USDA, CSRS, Vienna, Virginia. CC1992-2, June 1992. 19 pp.

This report recommends implementation of an innovative minoruse pesticides strategy before 1997, so as to assure the continued availability to U.S. consumers of high-quality, reasonably priced minor crops.

Pesticides in Surface and Ground Water.
Chair: R. Don Wauchope, USDA, ARS, University of Georgia Coastal Plain Experiment Station, Tifton. IP2, April 1994. 8 pp.

This report covers pesticide varieties, uses, and resulting pollution potential; relating concentrations in water resources to human and ecosystem risk; and risk mitigation.

Pesticides in the Diets of Infants and Children: Scientists' Review.
SP17, August 1993. 20 pp.

The five members of a Council on Agriculture, Science, and Technology task force who reviewed the National Research Council (NRC) report on pesticides in infants' and children's diets agree that the report is a thorough, balanced, and objective summary of available information on the subject. The NRC report called for improvements in the evaluation and regulation of pesticide risks in infants' and children's foods.

Preparing U.S. Agriculture for Global Climate Change.
Chair: Paul Waggoner, Connecticut Agricultural Experiment Station, New Haven. R119, June 1992. 96 pp.

This report covers all aspects of the subject, emphasizing adaptation to changes, emission of greenhouse gases, and the impact of climate change.

Public Perceptions of Agrichemicals.
Author: Eileen O. van Ravenswaay, Michigan State University, East Lansing. R123, January 1995. 35 pp.

The author writes about understanding public perceptions, risk perception and the public, risk acceptability and pesticides, and consumer perceptions of animal drugs.

Quality of U.S. Agricultural Products.
Chair: Lowell D. Hill, University of Illinois at Urbana-Champaign.
R126, February 1996. 286 pp.

Accurate assessment of the quality of agricultural products is essential in today's rapidly globalizing economy. A few changes in policies and regulations related to the quality of agricultural products could increase access to U.S. export and domestic markets.

Radiation Pasteurization of Food.
Cochairs: Donald W. Thayer, USDA, Agricultural Research Service, Wyndmoor, Pennsylvania, and Edward S. Josephson, University of Rhode Island, West Kingston. IP7, April 1996. 10 pp.

Foodborne bacteria cause as many as 9,000 deaths in the United States annually. Scientifically proven safe, low doses of pasteurizing radiation can kill over 99 percent of most foodborne bacteria. Radiation pasteurization safely controls foodborne pathogens on beef, pork, lamb, and seafood.

Reducing American Exposure to Nitrate, Nitrite, and Nitroso Compounds: The National Network to Prevent Birth Defects Proposal.
Author: Charles A. Black, Iowa State University, Ames. CC1989-1, June 1989. 16 pp.

This paper reviews the scientific literature on nitrates, concluding that there is inadequate evidence linking nitrate or nitrite ingestion to birth defects or to stomach cancer.

Risks and Benefits of Selenium in Agriculture.
Chair: James E. Oldfield, Department of Animal Sciences, Oregon State University, Corvallis. IP3, June 1994. 6 pp.

Scientists found no evidence that supplemental selenium use for farm animals and poultry, including feedlot concentrations, was involved in any environmental problems.

Sustainable Agriculture and the 1995 Farm Bill.
Authors: Neville P. Clarke and Paula B. Ford. SP18, April 1995. 32 pp.

This summary of a January 1995 conference sponsored by the Council on Agriculture, Science, and Technology includes discussion on the issues of legislation, environmental concerns, conservation, rural development, research, and education.

U.S. Agriculture and the North American Free Trade Agreement.
Chair: G. Edward Schuh, Dean, Hubert H. Humphrey Institute of Public Affairs, University of Minnesota, Minneapolis. CC1993-1, July 1993. 41 pp.

The members of a Council on Agriculture, Science, and Technology task force believe many of the fears about the North American Free Trade Agreement (NAFTA) are not well founded. There generally would be a gain to U.S. producers of grain, oilseeds, livestock, and possibly dairy, and losses for producers who compete with Mexican fruits and vegetables.

Waste Management and Utilization in Food Production and Processing.
Chairs: Larry L. Boersma, Department of Soil Science, Oregon State University, Corvallis, and Ishwar P. Murarka, Electric Power Research Institute. R124, October 1995. 125 pp.

This is a comprehensive report on wastes from crop production, poultry farms, swine production, cattle feedlots, dairy farms, food processing, and seafood production and processing.

Water Quality: Agriculture's Role.
Chair: Frank J. Humenik, North Carolina State University, Raleigh. R120, December 1992. 103 pp.

This report discusses modern agriculture's impacts on the environment, especially surface and ground water, and increases the understanding of the science, risks, benefits, and realities of agricultural production and water-quality protection.

The Well-Being of Agricultural Animals.
Chair: Stanley E. Curtis, Pennsylvania State University, University Park. R130, September 1997. 34 pp.

Concern for the welfare of farm animals is mounting in the United States. Although many of the issues of agricultural animal welfare probably will be resolved politically, the Council on Agriculture, Science, and Technology task force recommends that scientists become involved in clarifying the issue.

Wetland Policy Issues.
Chair: Jay A. Leitch, North Dakota State University, Fargo. CC1994-1, February 1994. 47 pp.

The author presents a definition of wetlands, their functions and values, agricultural conflicts, socioeconomic issues, conservation concepts, and conclusions in this report.

Other Readings

Animal Welfare Institute. *Animals and Their Legal Rights: A Survey of American Laws from 1641 to 1990.* 4th ed. Washington, DC: Animal Welfare Institute, 1990. 441 pp.

Bennett, Hugh Hammond. *Elements of Soil Conservation.* New York: McGraw-Hill, 1947. 358 pp.

————. *Soil Conservation.* New York: McGraw-Hill, 1939. 993 pp.

Bowler, I., ed. *The Geography of Agriculture in the Developed Market Economies.* London: Longman Scientific & Technical, 1992. 317 pp.

Bredahl, Maury E., Nicole Ballenger, and John C. Dunmore, eds. *Agriculture, Trade, and the Environment: Discovering and Measuring the Critical Linkages.* Boulder, CO: Westview Press, 1996. 311 pp.

Bryant, C., and T. Johnston. *Agriculture in the City's Countryside.* Toronto: University of Toronto Press, 1992. 233 pp.

Buzby, J. C., and R. C. Ready. "Do Consumers Trust Food-Safety Information?" *Food Review* (January–April 1996): 46–49.

Cohen, M. P. *The Pathless Way: John Muir and American Wilderness.* Madison, WI: University of Wisconsin Press, 1984. 408 pp.

Conley, H. H. "The 1995 Farm Bill: Opportunities and Challenges for Economists." *Journal of Agricultural and Applied Economics* 28: 1 (July 1996): 35–56.

Dunlap, T. R. *DDT: Scientists, Citizens, and Public Policy.* Princeton, NJ: Princeton University Press, 1981. 318 pp.

Ervin, D. E., and K. Smith. *What It Takes to "Get to Yes" for Whole Farm Planning Policy.* Policy Studies Report No. 5. Greenbelt, MD: Henry A. Wallace Institute for Alternative Agriculture, 1996. 42 pp.

Fox, S. R. *John Muir and His Legacy: The American Conservation Movement.* 1st ed. Boston: Little, Brown, 1981. 436 pp.

Hamilton, D. E. *From New Day to New Deal: American Farm Policy from Hoover to Roosevelt, 1928–1933.* Chapel Hill, NC: University of North Carolina Press, 1991. 333 pp.

Harris, Glenn R. "Public Acquisition versus Private Stewardship for Wetland Protection: An Evaluation of the St. Lawrence Valley National Wildlife Refuge, USA." *Journal of Environmental Planning and Management* 37 (1994): 3–19.

Hart, J. F. *The Land That Feeds Us.* New York: W. W. Norton, 1993. 398 pp.

Hill, B. *Farm Incomes, Wealth, and Agricultural Policy.* 2d ed. Brookfield, VT: Avebury, 1996. 292 pp.

Horowitz, John. "Preferences for Pesticide Regulation." *American Journal of Agricultural Economics* 76 (1994): 396–406.

Johnson, P. C. *Farm Inventions in the Making of America.* Des Moines, IA: Wallace-Homestead Book Co., 1976. 128 pp.

Jordan, T. G. "The Origins and Distribution of Open-Range Ranching." *Social Science Quarterly* 53 (1972): 105–121.

———. *Trails to Texas: Southern Roots of Western Cattle Ranching.* Lincoln, NE: University of Nebraska Press, 1981. 220 pp.

Kelso, M. M., W. E. Martin, and L. E. Mack. *Water Supplies and Economic Growth in an Arid Environment: An Arizona Case Study.* Tucson, AZ: University of Arizona Press, 1973. 327 pp.

Krimsky, Sheldon, and Roger P. Wrubel. *Agricultural Biotechnology and the Environment: Science, Policy, and Social Issues.* The Environment and the Human Condition Series. Urbana, IL: University of Illinois Press, 1996. 294 pp.

Lappe, Frances Moore. *Diet for a Small Planet.* New York: Ballantine Books, 1991. 479 pp.

Lawrence J. *The U.S. Pork Industry in Transition.* Iowa State University Staff Papers Series. Ames, IA: Iowa State University, 1992.

Leopold, Aldo. "The Farmer as a Conservationist." *American Forest* 45: 205–208.

Lockeretz, W., ed. *Visions of American Agriculture.* Ames, IA: Iowa State University Press, 1997. 243 pp.

Manchester, A., and D. Blayney. *The Structure of Dairy Markets: Past, Present, and Future.* Agricultural Economics Report No. 757. Washington, DC: U.S. Department of Agriculture, Economic Research Service, Commercial Agriculture Division, 1997. 52 pp.

Margolis, Howard. *Dealing with Risk: Why the Public and the Experts Disagree on Environmental Issues*. Chicago: University of Chicago Press, 1997. 227 pp.

Mather, E. C. "The American Great Plains." *Annals of the Association of American Geographers* 62 (1972): 237–257.

McMichael, P., ed. *The Global Restructuring of Agro-Food Systems*. Ithaca, NY: Cornell University Press, 1994. 303 pp.

Mellor, J. W. *Agriculture on the Road to Industrialization*. Baltimore, MD: Johns Hopkins University Press for the International Food Policy Research Institute, 1995. 358 pp.

Molnar, J. J., ed. *Agricultural Change: Consequences for Southern Farms and Rural Communities*. Boulder, CO: Westview Press, 1986. 440 pp.

Mungall, E., and W. Sheffield. *Exotics on the Range—The Texas Example*. College Station, TX: Texas A&M University Press, 1994. 265 pp.

Pasour, E., Jr., and F. Scrimgeour. "New Zealand Economic Reforms." *CHOICES* 10 (1995): 15–21.

Phillsbury, Richard, and John Florin. *Atlas of American Agriculture: The American Cornucopia*. Macmillan Library Reference Series. New York: Macmillan, 1996. 278 pp.

Pierce, J. "Towards the Reconstruction of Agriculture: Path of Change and Adjustment." *Professional Geographer* 46 (1994): 178–190.

Pisani, D. J. *From the Family Farm to Agribusiness: The Irrigation Crusade in California, 1850–1931*. Berkeley, CA: University of California Press, 1984. 521 pp.

Sampson, R. N. *For Love of the Land: A History of the National Association of Conservation Districts*. League City, TX: National Association of Conservation Districts, 1985. 338 pp.

Schumacher, Ernst Friedrich. *Small Is Beautiful: Economics as If People Mattered*. New York: Harper & Row, 1975. 305 pp.

Sheail, John. "The Regulation of Pesticide Use: An Historical Perspective." In *Innovation and Environmental Risk*, edited by Lewis Roberts and Albert Weale, 38–46. London: Belhaven Press, 1991.

Skaggs, J. M. *Prime Cut: Livestock Raising and Meatpacking in the United States, 1607–1983*. 1st ed. College Station, TX: Texas A&M University Press, 1986. 263 pp.

Smallwood, J. B. *Water in the West*. Manhattan, KS: Sunflower University Press, 1983. 86 pp.

Soule, J. D., and J. K. Piper. *Farming in Nature's Image: An Ecological Approach to Agriculture.* Washington, DC: Island Press, 1992. 286 pp.

Stewart, R. E. *Seven Decades That Changed America: A History of the American Society of Agricultural Engineers, 1907–1977.* St. Joseph, MO: American Society of Agricultural Engineers, 1979. 432 pp.

Stokes, S. N., and A. E. Watson. *Saving America's Countryside: A Guide to Rural Conservation.* 2d ed. Baltimore, MD: Johns Hopkins University Press, 1997. 447 pp.

Swanson, L. E., ed. *Agriculture and Community Change in the U.S.* Boulder, CO: Westview Press, 1988. 355 pp.

Thurman, W. N. *Assessing the Environmental Impact of Farm Policies.* Washington, DC: AEI Press, 1995. 79 pp.

Tuszynski, Carol, ed. "Current Trends and Uncertainties for the Future of U.S. Agriculture." Unpublished report. Fort Collins, CO: Center for Emerging Issues, Centers for Epidemiology and Animal Health, Veterinary Services, Animal and Plant Health Inspection Service, U.S. Department of Agriculture, 1998. 177 pp.

University of Maryland Cooperative Extension Service. *The Cooperative Extension System: A Response to America's Critical Concerns.* College Park, MD: University of Maryland Cooperative Extension Service, Department of Information and Publications, 1986.

Urquhart, J. *Animals on the Farm: Their History from the Earliest Times to the Present Day.* London: Macdonald & Co., 1983. 182 pp.

U.S. Department of Agriculture. *In Partnership with People and a Healthy Land.* Report PA-1540. Washington, DC: Natural Resources Conservation Service, 1996.

———. *A Productive Nation in Harmony with a Quality Environment— Soil Conservation Service Strategic Initiatives for the 1990s.* Washington, DC: Natural Resources Conservation Service, 1994. 8 pp.

———. *U.S. Farm Policies: Implications for the Future.* Washington, DC: U.S. Department of Agriculture, Economic Research Service, 1997. 16 pp.

U.S. Department of Agriculture, Economic Research Service. *International Agricultural Baseline Projections to 2005.* Agricultural Economic Report No. 750. Washington, DC: U.S. Department of Agriculture, 1997. 196 pp.

———. "USDA's 1997 Baseline: The Domestic Outlook to 2005." *Agricultural Outlook* (April 1997).

Van Kooten, G. C., J. Weisensel, P. Ward, and Duangdao Chinthammit. "Valuing Trade-Offs between Net Returns and Stewardship Practices: The Case of Soil Conservation in Saskatchewan." *American Journal of Agricultural Economics* 72 (1990): 104–113.

Willham, R. L. *The Legacy of the Stockman.* Ames, IA: Iowa State University, Winrock International, 1985. 174 pp.

Winsberg, M. D. "Agricultural Specialization in the United States since World War II." *Agricultural History* 56 (1982): 692–701.

Wolfe, R. *Farm Wars: The Political Economy of Agriculture and the International Trade Regime.* New York: St. Martin's Press, 1998. 235 pp.

Internet Sites

Today, a person can find just about any thing on the Internet. However, the Internet is not monitored for quality, consistency, or honesty. I have listed sites that I feel are helpful and worth visiting. Where possible, descriptions are taken directly from the Web sites, with small adaptations or additions where appropriate.

Farm and Ranch

Agricultural Marketing Service (AMS)
http://angus.interspeed.net/alot/opm.html

The AMS provides current, unbiased price and sales information to assist in the orderly marketing and distribution of farm commodities. Reports include information on prices, volume, quality, condition, and other market data on farm products. Both domestic and international markets are covered.

American Farm Bureau
http://www.fb.com/

See "Organizations," Chapter 5, for a complete description.

Animal Industry Foundation Online
http://www.aif.org/

See "Organizations," Chapter 5, for a complete description.

Center for Farm Financial Management
http://www.cffm.umn.edu:80/cffm/cffm.htm

The Center for Farm Financial Management develops educational tools for farmers, agricultural lenders, and educators to apply toward farm planning, financing, and analysis. Decisionmaking software includes financial-management planning, manure-application planning, dairy herd analysis, and rent calculators. Status reports, training schedules, and informative articles are provided in a quarterly newsletter.

National Cattlemen's Beef Association
http://www.beef.org/

See "Organizations," Chapter 5, for a complete description.

National Pork Producers Council
http://www.nppc.org

See "Organizations," Chapter 5, for a complete description.

Magazines and Trade Journals

A*L*O*T Angus Association: Publications On-Line
http://www.erinet.com/carl/opm.html

This site provides links to more than 200 on-line farm and ranch publications.

Agriculture Online (Successful Farming)
http://www.agriculture.com/

Operated by Successful Farming, this site provides current news on markets, weather, technology, and machinery. It also covers feature articles of interest to producers and provides a variety of Internet links and interaction tools for farmers, ranchers, and agribusinesses.

Farm Journal
http://www.farmjournal.com

The *Farm Journal* boasts 660,000 subscribers nationwide, giving it the largest circulation for a farm magazine. The Web site contains articles from the *Journal*, market news, weather, links to other agricultural sites, opinion polls, and other information for farm managers. Other magazines, such as *Beef Today* and *Hogs Today*, may also be accessed through this site.

High Plains Journal
http://www.hpj.com/

This is an electronic version of the weekly periodical and much more. News, articles, and classifieds focus on issues confronting agriculture in the High Plains states. The site is well organized and contains many practical links to markets, weather, and other useful information. Chat and discussion forums for agricultural professionals are included.

Homefarm
http://www.homefarm.com/

Homefarm has links to articles from several magazines and journals.

Progressive Farmer
http://www.progressivefarmer.com

An on-line version of the *Progressive Farmer* magazine, this site includes current news stories, links to other sites, market and weather news, and a general store.

Software

A*L*O*T Angus Association: Software and Hardware Related to Ag Links
http://angus.interspeed.net/alot/csh.html

A*L*O*T stands for Arkansas * Louisiana * Oklahoma * Texas. The Angus Association has compiled an extremely useful list of computer program links, including private and public sources. Some software is free.

Farmer's Software Association (FSA)
http://www.farmsoft.com/

FSA provides information about agricultural software and hardware products available to the agricultural community. These include whole-farm computing systems for farm accounting, crop and livestock recordkeeping, harvest processing, yield monitoring, and other precision programs for agricultural products.

Government Agencies and Private Centers

Agricultural Research Service (ARS)
http://www.ars.usda.gov/

The goal of the ARS is to conduct research in order to develop and transfer to farmers and ranchers solutions to agricultural problems. In addition, the ARS strives to disseminate information to ensure safe, high-quality food and other agricultural products. Information regarding current news, research, and job opportunities may be located at this site. In addition, a search system and a section of related links are provided.

Cooperative State Research, Education, and Extension Service (CSREES)
http://www.reeusda.gov/

CSREES represents the research and higher education functions of the former Cooperative State Research Service and the education and outreach functions of the former Extension Service. The CSREES Web site contains links to information about agricultural legislation and other current events. It also provides an extensive list of information, including Web sites and fact sheets, on topics from agribusiness to welfare reform. Information can also be found on job opportunities and current grants that the U.S. Department of Agriculture is funding.

Economic Research Service
http://www.econ.ag.gov

The Economic Research Service, a division of the U.S. Department of Agriculture, is an excellent source for economic analysis and information on agriculture, food, natural resources, and rural

America. The site contains current news, brief analyses, and in-depth analyses. It also contains numerous data files (spreadsheets) that can be downloaded directly and "state fact sheets" that summarize farm- and ranch-related information about the United States or a particular state (see Exhibit 2 in Chapter 4). This site is one of the best sources available for statistical information and descriptive analyses of current economic issues in the farm sector.

National Agricultural Library (NAL)
http://www.nal.usda.gov/

The NAL is a great source for any information about agriculture. AgNIC, AGRICOLA, and the entire NAL collection may be accessed.

Natural Resources Conservation Service, U.S. Department of Agriculture
http://www.nrcs.usda.gov

The Natural Resources Conservation Service is a federal agency that works in partnership with the American people to conserve and sustain our natural resources. The Web site contains links to technical resources, programs, policies, data, and a browser searchable by subject. The site is an excellent starting place to learn about soil conservation issues.

The Nature Conservancy
http://www.tnc.org

See "Organizations," Chapter 5, for a complete description.

U.S. Department of Agriculture (USDA)
http://www.usda.gov/

The USDA is the primary agency in the federal government responsible for agricultural issues. It oversees activities in a variety of areas, including: farm and foreign agricultural services; food, nutrition, and consumer services; food safety; marketing and regulatory programs; natural resources and environment; research, education, and economics; rural development; and the Alternative Agricultural Research and Commercialization Corporation. Links are provided to all sites that include information regarding agriculture and the U.S. government.

U.S. Environmental Protection Agency (EPA)
http://www.epa.gov

The home page for the EPA contains links to projects and programs, news and events, laws and regulations, publications, resources, databases and software, technical documents, teaching aids, and general information. This is a great place to find information about environmental resources, such as water and air, and to find discussions, articles, and research about hot environmental topics.

U.S. Fish and Wildlife Service
http://www.fws.gov/

The U.S. Fish and Wildlife Service is a bureau within the Department of the Interior that conserves, protects, and enhances fish and wildlife and their habitats. The site can lead you to information about land use, fish and wildlife, publications, current news, and links about public land issues.

Agricultural Link Locators

Agaccess
http://www.Mother.com/agaccess/Aglinks.html

This is a great source for finding many agricultural sites of various types.

AgriGator
http://gnv.ifas.ufl.edu/WWW/AGATOR_HOME.HTM

The University of Florida Institute of Food and Agricultural Sciences has developed and continually updates a comprehensive collection of local, national, and international agricultural resources in a Worldwide Agricultural Site Index.

AgriNet
http://agrinet.tamu.edu/

AgriNet is a service of the Texas A&M Agricultural Program developed to provide a single starting point to all agricultural resources on the Internet. The objective is to promote agribusiness and to enhance marketing and research for agricultural products.

AgriSurf!
http://www.agrisurf.com

AgriSurf! claims to be the world's largest searchable agricultural World Wide Web index. All the sites in AgriSurf! are handpicked by agricultural experts, not computer programmers. They have an array of Web robots to continually check the existence and content of these sites so that their links stay fresh.

Virtual Library
http://vlib.org

The Virtual Library is the oldest catalog of the Web, started by Tim Berners-Lee, the creator of the Web itself. It is run by a confederation of volunteers who compile pages of key links for particular areas in which they have expertise. The pages at this site have been presorted and selected because they are of high quality. It has a section on agriculture with many excellent links.

World Wide Web Sites of Interest to Agriculture
http://www.gennis.com/aglinks.html

This site contains several links to agricultural sites. The list of sites is broken into eight different categories: general agriculture; farms, ranches, and companies; associations; markets; magazines and newsletters; government; research and education; and weather.

Agricultural Policy and Trade

AgPolicy Wrap-Up
http://www.okstate.edu/OSU_Ag/asnr/agec/AgPolicy/

This site contains current news on issues in agricultural policy, links to other agricultural policy sites, and an archive of news covered during the last four months.

Center for Agriculture and Rural Development
http://www.ag.iastate.edu/card/

See "Organizations," Chapter 5, for a complete description.

Colorado State Government (and other states)
http://www.state.co.us

State governments have their own Web sites with links to their politicians and agencies. These sites usually also contain information about the state, tourism, and business. The address above is for Colorado; replace "co" with the appropriate two-letter code for other states.

Farm Bill Network
http://www.fb-net.org/

This site contains detailed information relating to the development and implementation of the Conservation Reserve Program, Wetland Reserve Program, Wetland Habitat Incentives Program, and other U.S. Department of Agriculture Farm Bill conservation programs and related programs benefiting fish and wildlife habitats, water quality, and other resources. The information is designed for use by personnel of state natural resource agencies, conservation and environmental nongovernmental organizations, and landowners. All individuals concerned with improving and protecting fish and wildlife habitats, water quality, soil productivity, and related resources will find helpful information.

Farm Foundation
http://www.farmfoundation.org/

See "Organizations," Chapter 5, for a complete description.

Food and Agricultural Policy Research Institute
http://www.fapri.missouri.edu/

This institute is partially funded by Congress to analyze the complex economic interrelationships of the food and agriculture industry. Baseline projections of farm statistics such as production and prices are their main product. The unit does two world agricultural baselines each year for the U.S. agricultural sector and for international commodity markets. This is the place to look for projections about the impacts of U.S. policy on the agricultural sector.

Institute for Agriculture and Trade Policy
http://www.iatp.org

See "Organizations," Chapter 5, for a complete description.

NAFTA Home Page: Department of Commerce
http://iep.doc.gov/nafta/nafta2.htm

A primary objective of the Office of NAFTA and Inter-American Affairs is to provide accurate and timely information to U.S. exporters experiencing market access barriers in Canada or Mexico. In an effort to better serve the business community, questions regarding commercial and economic conditions in Mexico or Canada, including tariff rates, are now being handled by the Trade Information Center and the nationwide U.S. Export Assistance Centers.

Issues and Concerns

Animal Behavior and Welfare Sites
http://www.wam.umd.edu/~jaguar/

Containing links to numerous animal behavior and animal welfare sites, this site offers information about both sides of the issue.

Animal Rights Resource Site
http://arrs.envirolink.org/

This site, which is part of the Envirolink network, is an extensive site with information about Internet links, news, jobs, and organizations. It also houses its own search engine.

Community Alliance with Family Farmers (CAFF)
http://www.caff.org/

Founded in 1978, CAFF is a nonprofit member-activist organization. CAFF political and educational campaigns are building a movement of rural and urban people who foster family-scale agriculture that cares for the land, sustains local economies, and promotes social justice. Members are urbanites, farmers, environmentalists, rural activists, students, and anyone concerned with the social and environmental dimensions of agriculture. The site includes information about public policy, sustainable agriculture, and community-supported agriculture.

Desdemona's Splash!
http://www.epa.gov/owow/NPS/kids/splash/webpage2/

Splash! is a water-quality computer game for kids that was developed through the U.S. Environmental Protection Agency. The production of Desdemona's Splash! was a collaborative effort that pooled the talents, resources, and expertise of staff and volunteers representing many local, state, and federal agencies and organizations. Browsers can download a free demonstration or buy a CD-ROM on-line. "Teachers and Kids Links" can be accessed from this page, which has links to several educational materials about water.

Environmental Working Group
http://www.ewg.org/

See "Organizations," Chapter 5, for a complete description.

Farm*A*Syst and Home*A*Syst
http://www.wisc.edu/farmasyst/

This voluntary program is a partnership between government agencies and private business that enables individuals to prevent pollution on farms, ranches, and homes using confidential environmental assessments. The Farm*A*Syst/Home*A*Syst formula of education, self-assessment, and action plans motivates rural, suburban, and urban residents to take voluntary action. Fact sheets pull legal and technical requirements into a format that non-experts can understand. Step-by-step worksheets enable individuals to apply site-specific management practices to their own property. The worksheets identify pollution risks from activities such as petroleum storage, waste disposal, and pesticide management that can threaten a family's health and financial security. Program materials help landowners locate the technical resources and financial assistance needed to implement action plans.

FarmAid
http://www.farmaid.com

See "Organizations," Chapter 5, for a complete description.

Farmland Information Library: American Farmland Trust
http://farm.fic.niu.edu/fic/home.html

This is an excellent site for issues related to farmland use. It includes literature, research results, law and policy, and an excellent set of fact sheets including right-to-farm laws, farmland preservation tools, agricultural zoning, and estate planning, among many others. It is primarily concerned with stewardship and sustainable development.

The Heartland Center for Leadership Development
http://www.4w.com/heartland/

The Heartland Center for Leadership Development is an independent, nonprofit organization developing local leadership that responds to the challenges of the future. Based in Nebraska, the Heartland Center was organized in 1985 by a group of Great Plains leaders as an outgrowth of Visions from the Heartland, a grassroots futures project. Today the center is known throughout North America for its field research on rural community survival and for its hands-on programs in community leadership development. Programs of the center emphasize that local capacity is critical— and renewing local leadership essential—as towns, cities, and states work to remain competitive today and in the future.

National Budget Simulation
http://garnet.berkeley.edu:3333/budget/budget.html

Try this just for fun—this site gives you the chance to make tradeoffs between national programs while trying not to create a new budget deficit. It can really open a person's eyes about how hard it is to make decisions between deserving programs.

Nonpoint Source Kids Page
http://www.epa.gov/owow/NPS/kids/

This page contains a variety of elementary materials for kids about water pollution from nonpoint sources such as agriculture. It is developed and maintained by the U.S. Environmental Protection Agency's Office of Water.

PETA Online
http://www.peta-online.org/index.html

People for the Ethical Treatment of Animals (PETA), with more than 600,000 members, is the largest animal rights organization in the world. PETA operates under the simple principle that animals are not ours to eat, wear, experiment on, or use for entertainment. PETA focuses its attention on the four areas in which the largest numbers of animals suffer the most intensely for the longest periods of time: on factory farms, in laboratories, in the fur trade, and in the entertainment industry. Other issues, including the cruel killing of beavers, birds, and other "pests," and the abuse of backyard dogs, are also targeted. PETA works through public education, cruelty investigations, research, animal rescue, legislation, special events, celebrity involvement, and direct action.

Rural Community Development Resources—Kellogg Collection
http://www.unl.edu/kellogg/index.html

High-quality rural community development materials funded by the Kellogg Foundation and other selected sponsors of recognized rural programs can be found here. Guidebooks, manuals, workshop materials, reports, books, and videos are included. A major benefit of this collection is its central repository for such materials to discourage new programs from spending time and money to develop resource materials that may already exist.

Rural Information Center: National Agricultural Library
http://www.nal.usda.gov:80/ric/

The Rural Information Center (RIC) is a joint project of the U.S. Department of Agriculture's Cooperative State Research, Education, and Extension Service and the National Agricultural Library (NAL). RIC provides information and referral services to local government officials, community organizations, health professionals and organizations, rural electric and telephone cooperatives, libraries, businesses, and rural citizens working to maintain the vitality of America's rural areas. The center combines the technical, subject matter expertise of the Extension Service's nationwide educational network with the information specialists and resources of the world's foremost agricultural library, the NAL.

Rural Policy Research Institute (RUPRI)
http://www.rupri.org/

RUPRI provides objective analysis and facilitates public dialogue concerning the impacts of public policy on rural people and places. Many policies that are not explicitly "rural policies" nevertheless have substantial implications for rural areas, and RUPRI is dedicated to understanding and articulating these implications.

Sierra Club
http://www.sierraclub.org/

See "Organizations," Chapter 5, for a complete description.

Soil and Water Conservation Society
http://www.swcs.org/

See "Organizations," Chapter 5, for a complete description.

Sustainable Farming Connection
http://metalab.unc.edu/farming-connection

This site helps farmers tame costs, add value to what they sell, and keep them informed of the latest news from the sustainable farming community. This is a good site to browse when looking for ways to increase farm profits while building healthy soil and protecting the environment.

U.S. Department of Agriculture Rural Development Program
http://www.4w.com/heartland/

This excellent overview site helps people find anything they want to know about rural development available on the Internet.

Agricultural Data and Information

1996 Agriculture Fact Book
http://www.usda.gov/factbook/contents.htm

Information such as the structure of the U.S. agriculture farming regions, net farm income, rural population, federal funding for rural area development, and more is listed here. The information is compiled and maintained by the U.S. Department of Agriculture.

Agricultural Statistics
http://www.mannlib.cornell.edu/

Indexes to agricultural statistics such as production levels, prices, population, farm income, and other farm financial data are provided.

Agriculture Network Information Center (AgNIC)
http://www.agnic.org/

AgNIC is a distributed network that provides access to agriculture-related information, subject area experts, and other resources.

Census of Agriculture
http://govinfo.kerr.orst.edu/ag-stateis.html

The Census of Agriculture, from the Census Bureau, provides a complete picture of the agricultural sector in the U.S. economy by county, state, or ZIP code for years 1982, 1987, and 1992.

National Agricultural Statistics Service (NASS)
http://www.usda.gov/nass/

The mission of NASS is to serve the United States, its agriculture, and its rural communities by providing meaningful, accurate, and objective statistical information and services. American agriculture is continually counted, measured, priced, analyzed, and reported to provide the facts needed by people working throughout this vast industry. NASS publications cover a wide range of subjects, from traditional crops, such as corn and wheat, to specialties, such as mushrooms and flowers; from new calves to hogs slaughtered; from agricultural prices to land in farms. The abundance of information produced has earned for NASS employees the title, "The Fact Finders of Agriculture." Information is organized under publications, graphs, historic data, and census of agriculture. It has a text search feature and a place for kids facts. *Note:* The new agricultural census (1997) came out in February 1999. At the time of publication of this book, the raw data and cursory summaries at this site had not been used to update the Census of Agriculture site mentioned above.

U.S. Census Bureau
http://www.census.gov/

This site provides information and statistics from each census that it performs. It includes information about when each census will be performed, and it contains a search feature so that viewers can access the results of a census more quickly and easily.

U.S. State Fact Sheets

http://www.econ.ag.gov/epubs/other/usfact/

This site has fact sheets about every state regarding several basic issues, such as population and employment percentages.

USDA Economics and Statistics System

http://usda.mannlib.cornell.edu/usda/usda.html

The Economics and Statistics System contains nearly 300 reports and data sets from the economics agencies of the U.S. Department of Agriculture. These materials cover U.S. and international agriculture and related topics. Most reports are text files that contain time-sensitive information. Most data sets are in spreadsheet format and include time-series data that are updated yearly. The site includes a help button users can click for more introductory system information.

USDA Natural Resource Conservation Service: Maps, Facts, and Figures

http://www.nhq.nrcs.usda.gov/land/index/intro.html

This site contains an assortment of color graphics about agriculture and natural resources. It includes soil erosion, water quality, soil quality, productivity, wildlife, wetlands, and a host of other graphics about natural resources in the United States.

Glossary
of Terms

agrarian ideology An ideology that is friendly or based in agriculture.

anthropocentric A philosophy that people's decisions are centered on human desires.

aquaculture The production of aquatic plants or animals in a controlled environment.

biocentric A philosophy that people make decisions in harmony with the environment, rather than for selfish human wants.

biodiversity The variety of life and its processes. It includes the variety of living organisms, the genetic differences among them, and the communities and ecosystems in which they occur.

biotechnology The use of technology, based on living systems, to develop products for commercial and other purposes. Examples include plant regeneration and gene manipulation and transfer.

BST *(Bovine somatotropin)* A protein hormone produced naturally in the pituitary glands of cattle used to increase milk production in dairy cows. Also called BGH for bovine growth hormone.

bushel One bushel of wheat, soybeans, or potatoes weighs 60 pounds, or 27.2 kilograms, or 0.027 metric tons; one bushel of corn, grain sorghum, or rye weighs 56 pounds, or 25.4 kilograms, or 0.025 metric tons; one bushel of barley, buckwheat, or apples weighs 48 pounds, or 21.8 kilograms, or 0.022 metric tons; one bushel of oats weighs 32 pounds, or 14.5 kilograms, or 0.015 metric tons.

census of agriculture A count taken of the number of farms, land in farms, crop acreage, production information, farm value, and farm products. The census is taken every five years; the last one was in 1997.

conservation compliance A provision originally authorized by the Food Security Act of 1985 (PL 99-198) that requires farmers who operate highly erodible land to manage this land under an approved conservation system in order to maintain eligibility in various specified federal farm programs. The 1996 farm bill retains the conservation compliance provisions.

conservation plan A combination of land uses and practices to protect and improve soil productivity and to prevent soil erosion. A conservation plan must be approved by local conservation districts for acreage offered in the Conservation Reserve Program. The plan sets forth the conservation measures and maintenance that the farm owner or farm operator will carry out during the term of the contract.

Conservation Reserve Program (CRP) A program created by the Food Security Act of 1985 to reduce erosion and protect water quality on up to 45 million acres of farmland. Landowners agree to convert environmentally sensitive land to approved permanent conserving uses for 10 to 15 years in exchange for an annual rental payment and 50 percent of the cost of establishing permanent vegetative cover.

conservation tillage Cultivation methods that preserve more soil than conventional moldboard plows.

contract farming Producing goods or services for a fixed price and/or quantity.

crop rotation The practice of growing different crops in succession on the same land.

cross-compliance Requirements for some government farm-assistance programs that restrict benefits to those who comply with all commodity programs applicable to a given farm as a condition of program eligibility for any single commodity.

cultivator *See* farmer.

disaster payments Payments to producers of feed grains, wheat, rice, upland cotton, peanuts, soybeans, sugarcane, and sugar beets whose crops are subjected to natural disasters such as drought or flood.

ecosystem management A collaborative process to conserve ecological integrity and biodiversity.

Environmental Conservation Acreage Reserve Program (ECARP) An umbrella program authorized in 1990. It includes the Conservation Reserve Program (CRP) and the Wetlands Reserve Program (WRP). The 1996 farm bill continues the CRP and WRP and creates the Environmental Quality Incentives Program (EQIP).

Environmental Quality Incentives Program (EQIP) A program created by the 1996 farm bill to provide technical, educational, and cost-share assistance programmed at reducing soil, water, and related natural resource problems. The program replaces the Agricultural Conservation Program, the Water Quality Incentives Program, the Great Plains Conservation Program, the Colorado Salinity Control Program, and the Rural Environmental Conservation Program. EQIP is authorized at $1.3 billion over seven years, with at least half of the funding targeted for environmental concerns associated with livestock production.

erosion The process in which water or wind moves soil from one location to another.

externality A situation in which the action of one person affects another in a way that is not accounted for by any usual market activity. Externalities can be positive (scenic views) or negative (pollution).

farm Beginning in 1978, the U.S. Bureau of the Census defines a farm as any place that has $1,000 or more in gross sales of farm products per year. The previous definition (used for the 1959, 1964, 1969, and 1974 censuses) counted as a farm any place with less than ten acres from which $250 or more of agricultural products were sold, or normally would have been sold, during the census year. The definition changed again in the 1997 census to include any place from which $1,000 or more of agricultural products were produced and sold, or normally would have been sold, during the reference year.

farm bill The popular, generic term given to current federal legislation for agriculture. (*See* Food Security Act of 1985; Food, Agriculture, Conservation, and Trade Act of 1990; and Federal Agriculture Improvement and Reform Act [1996].)

Farm Service Agency A U.S. Department of Agriculture agency that administers commodity price and income support, farm loans, and resource conservation programs through a network of state and county offices.

farmer A person that produces a commodity on a land base. Usually a farmer produces a crop, but USDA and other government agencies often use farmer synonymously with cultivator, agriculturist, or rancher.

Farmland Protection Program A program established by the 1996 farm bill to fund the purchase of conservation easements of 170,000–340,000 acres of land having prime or unique soil or other desirable production qualities that are threatened by urban development. Eligibility depends on having a pending offer from a state or local government to protect qualifying land by limiting nonagricultural use.

Federal Agriculture Improvement and Reform Act (FAIR) The 1996 farm bill authorized by Congress and signed by the president, which will be in effect until 2002. It removed the link between income-support payments and farm prices through production-flexibility contracts. Previous farm bills had authorized payments to producers of program crops (wheat, cotton, corn, rice, and other feed grains) based on normal production. Farmers therefore had to continue producing program crops regardless of market conditions. FAIR will pay farmers no matter what they produce (with some limitations and restrictions), thus giving them production flexibility. However, since they are free to produce whatever they wish, payments will be phased out, weaning producers off direct government assistance. In 1998 and 1999, market conditions were so poor that prices fell below preset protection levels. Farmers received massive government payments, dashing the hope of many that producers can live without government aid.

Federal Crop Insurance Program A subsidized insurance program providing farmers with a means to manage the risk of crop losses resulting from natural disasters. The 1996 farm bill continues the Federal Crop Insurance Program, but eliminates (1) the requirement that producers purchase crop insurance to be eligible for farm program benefits and (2) the dual delivery of federal and private crop insurance in areas that have adequate access to private crop insurance providers.

Federal Insecticide, Fungicide, and Rodenticide Act The federal law governing the registration and use of agricultural chemicals.

fertilizer Any organic or inorganic material that is added to soil to provide nutrients for plant growth.

Food, Agriculture, Conservation, and Trade Act of 1990 This farm bill rovided a five-year framework for the secretary of agriculture to administer various agricultural and food programs. The act froze minimum target prices and allowed more planting flexibility. New titles included rural development, forestry, fruit and vegetable, grain quality, organic certification, global climate change, and commodity promotion programs.

Food Security Act of 1985 This farm bill provided a five-year framework for the secretary of agriculture to administer various agricultural and food programs. Introduced first serious programs to require environmental cross-compliance to get farm program benefits.

Food Stamp Program (FSP) A program that supplements the food-buying power of eligible low-income households by providing them with monthly benefits through coupons or Electronic Benefit Transfer (EBT) cards. EBT is an electronic system that allows food stamp recipients to transfer their benefits from a federal account to the retailer to pay for products without the use of coupons.

foodborne diseases (Buzby and Roberts 1996, p. 21)

> **Campylobacter jejuni** Campylobacteriosis ranges from a mild illness with diarrhea lasting a day to severe abdominal pain, severe diarrhea (sometimes bloody), sometimes accompanied by fever, oc-

casionally lasting for several weeks. The incubation period for most cases is two to five days, and the illness usually lasts from two to ten days, depending on its severity. Although the illness is generally regarded as a relatively mild disease, death can occur in some cases, especially for the very young, very old, or immunocompromised.

Clostridium perfringens   *C. perfringens* intoxication typically occurs 6 to 24 hours after ingestion of food that bears large counts of this bacteria. The illness in humans is frequently a mild gastrointestinal distress, lasting only around a day. Deaths are uncommon.

Escherichia coli   *E. coli* O157:H7 disease is usually a mild gastrointestinal illness that occurs three to five days after eating contaminated food. Severe complications, however, can arise. Hemorrhagic colitis is distinguished by the sudden onset of severe abdominal cramps, little or no fever, and diarrhea that may become grossly bloody. Although less than 5 percent of *E. coli* disease cases develop hemolytic uremic syndrome (HUS), it is a severe, life-threatening illness. HUS is a disease characterized by red blood-cell destruction, kidney failure, and neurological complications, such as seizures and strokes. Most HUS cases are children under five years old, although the feeble elderly may also be at risk.

Listeria monocytogenes   Listeriosis may be either mild or severe. Milder cases are characterized by a sudden onset of fever, severe headache, vomiting, and other influenza-type symptoms. Listeriosis may appear mild in healthy adults and more severe in fetuses, the elderly, and the immunocompromised. Outbreak data show that the incubation period ranges from 3 to 70 days. Women infected with Listeria during pregnancy may transmit the relatively mild disease. Death can occur in severe cases.

Staphylococcus aureus   *S. aureus* intoxication usually occurs within one to six hours following consumption of the toxins produced by the bacteria, but it may occur within 30 minutes. Illness caused by *S. aureus* enterotoxin is characterized by severe nausea, vomiting, cramps, and diarrhea. Although the illness generally does not last longer than one or two days, the severity of the illness may indicate the need for hospitalization.

Toxoplasma gondii   Toxoplasmosis can cause mild flulike symptoms, though most people infected with the parasite do not have any symptoms. People vary in their risk of getting sick from this parasite. People with suppressed immune systems, such as AIDS and cancer patients, face higher risks. One outbreak associated with undercooked meat indicates that the incubation period ranges from 10 to 23 days. Women infected with *T. gondii* during pregnancy may transmit the infection to their fetus, possibly leading to stillbirths or babies born with birth defects ranging from hearing or visual impairments to mental retardation.

freedom to farm A term used to describe the market orientation of the 1996 farm bill. Farmers can now plant almost whatever they wish without risking the loss of their government payments.

Fund for Rural America A fund established by the 1996 farm bill to augment existing resources for agricultural research and rural development.

General Agreement on Tariffs and Trade (GATT) An agreement originally negotiated in Geneva, Switzerland, in 1947 to increase international trade by reducing tariffs and other trade barriers. The agreement provides a code of conduct for international commerce and a framework for periodic multilateral negotiations on trade liberalization and expansion. The Uruguay Round Agreement established the World Trade Organization (WTO) to replace the institutions created by the GATT.

genetically modified organism Plants that have had certain genes implanted to make them resistant to pesticides, disease, or insects.

government payments Payments to producers authorized under various federal government programs. They include commodity price support payments, payments for diverting land from crop production to conserving uses or to nonsurplus crops, and payments to implement conservation practices. Government payments have been variously called direct payments, compensatory payments, income payments, diversion payments, set-aside payments, and deficiency payments.

Green Revolution A period of rapid increases in crop yields associated with intensive research to reduce hunger. The concept began in the 1940s in Mexico. In 1944, Mexico imported half the wheat it consumed; in 1956, it was self-sufficient through its own production. By the late 1960s, dramatic increases in yields were being realized in India, Pakistan, and other developing countries. Norman Borlaug won a Nobel prize in 1970 for his contribution to these successes. The Green Revolution is credited with saving millions of people from starvation, but it is also criticized for relying on fertilizers, pesticides, and other technologies that the poor cannot afford and that may lead to environmental degradation.

gross farm income Income that farm operators realize from farming. It includes cash receipts from the sale of farm products, value of food and fuel produced and consumed on farms, and the rental value of farm dwellings.

gross national product (GNP) A measure of the market value of goods and services produced by a nation. GNP includes receipts from the nation's business operations in foreign countries as well as the share of reinvested earnings in foreign affiliates of domestic corporations.

Hazard Analysis and Critical Control Point (HACCP) HACCP is a system of process control that can be used to prevent hazards to food by control, reduction, and prevention of pathogens. Effective January 1998, about 75 percent of the nation's raw meat and poultry products are in a HACCP system. HACCP emphasizes prevention by building in safety controls.

herbicide Any chemical used to destroy plants, especially weeds.

highly erodible cropland Cropland that meets specific conditions primarily relating to its land or soil classification and current or potential rate of erosion.

hypoxia A low-oxygen condition in the water that occurs where a free flowing body of water (like a river) enters a larger body of water, resulting in the rapid growth of plankton/phytoplankton that subsequently die and, in the process, consume large amounts of oxygen.

industrial crops Crops, such as industrial rapeseed, kenaf, meadowfoam, jojoba, lesquerella, guayule, and canola, that have industrial applications. Meadowfoam, jojoba, and lesquerella yield oils that can be used by industry.

industrialization The application of modern industrial manufacturing, production, procurement, distribution, and coordination concepts to the food and industrial product chain. (Boehlje 1996, p. 30)

Integrated Farm Management Program (IFMP) A program authorized in the 1990 farm bill to assist producers in adopting resource-conserving crop rotations by protecting participants' base acreage, payment yields, and program payments. The program's goal was to enroll 3 to 5 million acres over five years.

integrated pest management An integrated approach to controlling plant pests using careful monitoring of pests and weeds. It may include use of natural predators, chemical agents, and crop rotations.

irradiation A process that exposes food to ionizing radiation that injures or kills harmful bacteria. There are three types permitted; gamma rays, high-energy electrons, and x-rays.

Land-Retirement Program A multiyear voluntary government program to take cropland out of production. The land idled must be planted to soil-conserving cover crops or trees. The government generally pays the landowner an annual rental fee plus the cost of establishing a cover crop or trees. *See also* Conservation Reserve Program.

market failure A situation where the market does not provide optimal social solutions. This includes externalities and public goods. For example, a person who pollutes a river in the process of production does not pay the full cost of his or her actions. Someone downstream pays to clean up the water or loses value by tolerating dirtier water. Therefore, the market fails to correctly price the goods produced upstream. It actually costs more than the firm pays to produce it. Market failures lead to misallocation of resources.

net farm income A measurement of the profit or loss associated with a given year's production. Net farm income equals the difference between gross farm income and total expenses.

nonpoint source pollution Pollution that enters the environment from broad areas via water and runoff from a field or feedlot, such as areas in which fertilizers or other chemicals have been applied or animal manure is deposited, rather than from concentrated discharge points.

North American Free Trade Agreement (NAFTA) Ratified in 1993, this regional trade agreement between the United States, Canada, and Mexico requires that most agricultural tariffs be eliminated by January 1998; agreement not to use export subsidies in bilateral trade; and, between the United States and Mexico, to phase out all tariffs, quotas, and licenses that are barriers to agricultural trade within 15 years.

organic farming A production system that completely or mostly excludes the use of synthetically compounded fertilizers, pesticides, or growth regulators.

parity price A price for an individual commodity such that it would purchase, on a given date, a quantity of a standard list of goods equal to those that could have been bought at prevailing prices in a base period. For example, agricultural producers claim that parity today is around 50 percent, compared with the "Golden Era" of agriculture in 1910–1914. Therefore, they get half as much back for each dollar of input as was earned in the base period. However, they also get more than three times the yield today, which means they need only about 30 percent parity to be equally well off. A 50 percent parity implies that producers receive prices for their products that make them half as well off as farmers in the Golden Era.

pesticide residue A detectable level of chemical residue found on a food product.

pesticide tolerance levels Scientifically acceptable level of a pesticide residue that can exist on a fruit or vegetable product. Usually expressed in parts per million or billion.

point-source pollution Pollution originating from a distinct source, such as the outflow from a pipe or concentrated animal production facility.

public good Public goods have two characteristics. First, they are nonexcludable, meaning that once they are produced, it is impossible or very costly to exclude any one from use. Second, public goods are nonconsumptive, meaning that one person's enjoyment of the good does not diminish its availability for others. Few public goods are provided in the private sector. The government may provide them because the market failed to do so.

Public Law 480 (PL 480) The common name for the Agricultural Trade Development and Assistance Act of 1954, which seeks to expand foreign markets for U.S. agricultural products, combat hunger, and encourage economic development in developing countries. Also called the Food for Peace Program.

ranch A place where livestock is raised.

rancher A person who raises livestock, such as beef or sheep, on an expansive land base. Could also include buffalo, elk, or deer. Usually, a rancher takes advantage of ruminant livestock's ability to convert grass from rangeland into a product fit for human consumption. *See also* farmer.

rangeland Land that is predominantly grasses, grasslike plants, or shrubs suitable for grazing.

social costs The welfare (income, utility, satisfaction, etc.) losses to some group or groups of citizens. For example, high food prices would impose a social cost on the poor because their nutritional health would decline.

subsidy A direct or indirect benefit granted by a government for the production or distribution (including export) of a good or to supplement other services.

sustainable agriculture An integrated system of farming that will, over the long term, satisfy food and fiber needs, enhance environmental quality, make the most efficient use of resources, sustain the economic viability of farm operations, and enhance the quality of life.

swampbuster A provision in the 1985, 1990, and 1996 farm bills that discourages the conversion of natural wetlands to cropland use. Producers converting a wetland area to cropland lose eligibility for several federal farm-program benefits.

transgenic A crop that has another crop's gene transplanted into it.

Uruguay Round The Uruguay Round of Multilateral Trade Negotiations (UR) under the auspices of the GATT is a trade agreement designed to open world agricultural markets. The UR agriculture agreement covers four areas: export subsidies, market access, internal supports, and sanitary and phytosanitary rules. The agriculture agreement is being implemented over a six-year period, 1995–2000.

vertical integration A form of market control under which a single organization controls, via ownership or contractual arrangement, two or more adjacent stages in the production and/or marketing of a commodity.

Water Quality Protection Program A program authorized in the 1990 farm bill that provides incentive payments to farmers of up to $3,500 per year to adopt water quality improvement practices on cropland acres near wellheads, in areas inhabited by threatened or endangered species, or where agricultural production poses a threat to underground or surface water quality. Cost-sharing funds to adopt approved practices are also available, with priority given to producers who improve wildlife habitat.

wetlands   Land that is characterized by an abundance of moisture and that is inundated by surface or groundwater, often enough to support a prevalence of vegetation typically adapted for life in saturated soil conditions.

Wetlands Reserve Program (WRP)   A program authorized in 1990 that provides long-term protection of wetlands. Producers must agree to implement an approved wetlands restoration and protection plan and provide either a permanent easement or one of 30 years or more. In return for participating they receive payments over a 5- to 20-year period. The 1996 food bill maintains the maximum WRP total at 975,000 acres.

Wildlife Habitat Incentives Program   A program established by the 1996 farm bill to promote voluntary implementation of various on-farm management practices to improve wildlife habitat. Cost-sharing will be available with funding authorized at $50 million for fiscal years 1996–2002 from Conservation Reserve Program funds.

Specialty Terms for Farmland Protection

(Adapted from American Farmland Trust, http://farm.fic.niu.edu/fic-ta/tafs-gloss.html)

agricultural conservation easement (ACE)   A legal agreement restricting development on farmland. Land subjected to an ACE is generally restricted to farming and open space use. *See also* conservation easement.

agricultural district   A legally recognized geographic area formed by one or more landowners and approved by one or more government agencies, designed to keep land in agriculture. Agricultural districts are created for fixed, renewable terms. Enrollment is voluntary; landowners receive a variety of benefits that may include eligibility for differential assessment, limits on annexation and eminent domain, protection against unreasonable government regulation and private nuisance lawsuits, and eligibility for purchase of agricultural conservation easement programs. Also known as agricultural preserves, agricultural security areas, agricultural preservation districts, agricultural areas, agricultural incentive areas, agricultural development areas, and agricultural protection areas.

agricultural protection zoning (APZ)   Zoning is a form of local land-use regulation. Agricultural protection zoning ordinances protect the agricultural land base by limiting nonfarm uses, prohibiting high-density development, requiring houses to be built on small lots, and restricting subdivision of land into parcels that are too small to farm.

buffers   Physical barriers that separate farms from land uses that are incompatible with agriculture. Buffers help safeguard farms from vandals and trespassers and protect homeowners from some of the negative impacts of commercial farming. Vegetated buffers and topographic barriers reduce the potential for clashes between farmers and their nonfarming neighbors. Buffers may be required by local zoning ordinances.

cluster zoning A form of zoning that allows houses to be built close together in areas where large minimum lot sizes are generally required. By grouping houses on small sections of a large parcel of land, cluster zoning can be used to protect open space. Also known as cluster development, land preservation subdivision, open land subdivision, and open space subdivision.

community supported agriculture (CSA) A form of direct marketing of farm products that involves customers paying the farmer in advance for a weekly share of the harvest. Customers are often called shareholders. In some cases, shareholders may participate in farmwork and farm decisions. Farms that use this marketing strategy are called "CSA farms" or "CSAs." CSA is also known as subscription farming.

comprehensive growth management A state, regional, county, or municipal government program to control the timing, location, and character of land development.

conservation easement Legally recorded, voluntary agreements that limit land to specific uses. Easements may apply to entire parcels of land or to specific parts of the property. Most are permanent; term easements impose restrictions for a limited number of years. Land protected by conservation easements remains on the tax rolls and is privately owned and managed; landowners who donate permanent conservation easements are generally entitled to tax benefits. *See also* agricultural conservation easement *and* purchase of agricultural conservation easements.

deferred taxation A method to assess property values at lower rates to reduce farmers' tax bills. Deferred taxation permits eligible land to be assessed at its value for agriculture instead of at its actual value. Deferred taxations are similar to preferential assessment, but landowners must pay back some or all of the taxes that were excused if they later convert the farmland back to ineligible uses. For example, an orange grower in Florida might not be able to hold onto his land if he had to pay taxes based on its regular market value. He can pay lower taxes based on the agricultural value as long as he doesn't sell it to developers, in which case he then must pay back to the government the taxes he saved while claiming the land for farming.

development rights Development rights entitle property owners to develop land in accordance with local land-use regulations, which can be structured to encourage desirable development. In some jurisdictions, these rights may be sold to public agencies or qualified nonprofit organizations through a purchase of agricultural conservation easement or development rights programs. Development rights can be purchased, for example, from a farmer in an agreement that gave him the right to farm but not the right to develop his property for homes.

differential assessment An agricultural property tax relief program that allows eligible farmland to be assessed at its value for agriculture rather than its fair market value, which reflects "highest and best" use.

Farm Link A program that matches retiring farmers who want to keep their land in agriculture with beginning farmers who want to buy a farm. Farm Link programs are designed to facilitate farm transfer, usually between farmers who are not related to each other. Also known as Land Link.

generally accepted agricultural and management practices (GAAMP) Agricultural practices that are widely used by farmers; are promoted by agricultural institutions such as the Cooperative Extension Service; and comply with federal and state environmental, health, and safety laws and regulations. Some states have specific definitions of GAAMPs that may be used to determine whether a particular farm practice constitutes a public or private nuisance.

land trust A private, nonprofit conservation organization formed to protect natural resources such as productive farm and forest land, natural areas, historic structures, and recreational areas. Land trusts purchase and accept donations of conservation easements. They educate the public about the need to conserve land, and some provide land-use and estate-planning services to local governments and individual citizens.

preferential assessment A form of differential assessment that permits eligible land to be assessed at its value for agriculture.

purchase of agricultural conservation easements (PACE) PACE programs pay farmers to keep their land available for agriculture. Landowners sell an agricultural conservation easement to a qualified public agency or private conservation organization. Landowners retain full ownership and use of their land for agricultural purposes. PACE programs do not give government agencies the right to develop land. Development rights are extinguished in exchange for compensation. PACE is also known as purchase of development rights (PDR) and as agricultural preservation restriction (APR) in Massachusetts.

right-to-farm law A state law or local ordinance that protects farmers and farm operations from public and private nuisance lawsuits. A private nuisance interferes with an individual's use and enjoyment of his or her property. Public nuisances involve actions that injure the public at large.

taking An illegal government appropriation of private property or property rights. Traditionally, takings law has addressed physical seizures of land, but regulations that deprive landowners of certain property rights may also result in a taking in special circumstances. Courts decide whether a particular government action constitutes a taking.

transfer of development rights program (TDR) A program that allows landowners to transfer the right to develop one parcel of land to a different parcel of land to prevent farmland conversion. TDR programs establish "sending areas" where land is to be protected by agricultural conservation easements and "receiving areas" where land may be developed at a higher density than would otherwise be allowed by local zoning. Landowners in the sending area sell development rights to landowners in the receiving area, generally through the private market. When the development rights are sold on a parcel, a conservation easement is recorded and enforced by the local government. In some cases, the local government may establish a "TDR bank" to buy and sell development rights. The development rights created by TDR programs are referred to as transferable development rights (TDRs) or transferable development credits (TDCs).

urban growth boundary A theoretical line drawn around a community that defines an area to accommodate anticipated growth for a given period of time, generally 20 years. Urban growth boundaries are a growth-management technique designed to prevent sprawl. They are often used to guide decisions on infrastructure development, such as the construction of roads and the extension of municipal water and sewer services.

References

American Farmland Trust. http://farm.fic.niu.edu/fic-ta/tafs-gloss.html

Boehlje, M. "Industrialization of Agriculture: What Are the Implications?" *CHOICES* 11 (First quarter, 1996): 30–33.

Buzby, J., and T. Roberts. "ERS Updates U.S. Foodborne Disease Costs for Seven Pathogens." *Food Review* (September–December 1996): 21.

Other Glossaries Used for Reference

Hallberg, M. C. *American Agriculture: Choices and Consequences.* Ames, IA: Iowa State University Press, 1992. 374 pp.

Lipton, Kathryn, and Susan Pollack. "Major Agricultural and Trade Legislation, 1933–96." In *Provisions of the Federal Agricultural Improvement and Reform Act of 1996.* Agriculture Information Bulletin, appendix III, AIB-729 (1996): 128–138. Washington, DC: U.S. Department of Agriculture, Economic Research Service, 1996.

Index